Praise for Terry Lyles and *Performance under Pressure*

"Performance under Pressure *combines modern psychology with biometric data to create a holistic approach to maximizing performance in any environment. Utilizing data as a tool adds a unique and critical component, broadening the perspective of the process for personal performance management and improved outcomes.*"

—Al Marco, PhD, CEO, PhitTech/WelHealth

"Terry is an important part of our race team. He brings a positive thought process to any situation and keeps our key crew members and drivers focused on what is important: performance!"

—Ray Evernham, Founder, Evernham Motorsports, NASCAR Hall of Fame Crew Chief

"As an NBA referee and founder of Mauer Sports Nutrition, I deal with conflict resolution and have to make difficult business decisions daily. We live in a fast-paced world, and my good friend Terry Lyles gives people the tools they need to cope with stressful situations. I highly recommend his book to anyone seeking to perform at a high level while facing the pressures of everyday life."

—Kenny Mauer, NBA Referee, Founder of Mauer Sports Nutrition

"Dr. Terry Lyles has found the formula to help all of us live above our fears, our frustrations, and the anxieties that life's storms often bring."

—Robert Polito, Former Penn State Football Player

*"Dr. Terry Lyles . . . is so full of wisdom and truth. . . .
He pulls this wisdom from his huge pot of life experiences
and research and blesses all the people around him with
sage advice and wonderful encouragement."*

—John Li, MD, ENT, Allergy Associates of Florida

*"We are pleased to have Dr. Lyles on board with the
Doug Herbert racing team. He brings with him principles
and ideas that maximize the potential of all our team
members and ultimately will help us get to the finish
line ahead of our competition at over 330 mph!"*

—Doug Herbert, NHRA Top Fuel Driver and Founder of B.R.A.K.E.S.
(putonthebrakes.org)

*"If you think you are beaten, you are; if you'd like to win but
think you can't, it's almost certain you won't. Life's battles don't
always go to the strongest or the fastest, but sooner or later the
one who wins is the one who believes and* never *gives up. . . .
Dr. Terry Lyles [has helped] me to understand the pressures
and stress when life's spotlight is on me to excel.
He has catapulted me to the next level in my life and
in my athletic performance on pit road!"*

—Ed Watkins, Gasman for NASCAR Sprint Cup Target #42 Car

PERFORMANCE UNDER PRESSURE

CRACK YOUR PERSONAL STRESS CODE
AND LIVE THE LIFE OF YOUR DREAMS

PERFORMANCE UNDER PRESSURE

CRACK YOUR PERSONAL STRESS CODE AND LIVE THE LIFE OF YOUR DREAMS

TERRY LYLES, PHD
AMERICA'S STRESS COACH

SWC PRESS

DR. TerryLyles

Dr. Terry Lyles holds a PhD in psychology and is recognized as an international educator, author, and speaker to universities, schools, Fortune 500 companies, world-class athletes, and public audiences. He teaches groups of all ages how to navigate life's storms and enhance performance through integrating psychological and physiological tools, metrics, and practices.

info@TerryLyles.com
TerryLyles.com

Medical disclaimer: The medical and health information and coaching in this book are based on the training, experience, and research of the author and are intended to inform and educate. Because each person and situation is unique, the reader should check with a qualified health professional before following this or any program. The author and publisher specifically disclaim any liability, loss, or risk, personal or otherwise, that is incurred as a consequence, directly or indirectly, of the use and application of the contents of this book.

Most Southwestern Consulting books are available at special quantity discounts for bulk purchases for sales promotions, premiums, fund-raising, or educational use. Special books or book excerpts can be created to fit specific needs at the compliance of the author. For details, write media@southwesternconsulting.com.

ISBN: 978-0-578-50437-7
Library of Congress Control Number available upon request
Printed in the United States of America
10 9 8 7 6 5 4 3 2

SWC PRESS

Performance under Pressure: Crack Your Personal Stress Code and Live the Life of Your Dreams was developed by Terry Lyles in cooperation with Southwestern Consulting and Southwestern Publishing House: 2451 Atrium Way, Nashville, TN 37214. Southwestern Consulting and Southwestern Publishing House, Inc., are wholly owned subsidiaries of Southwestern, Inc., Nashville, TN.

Southwestern Speakers is a division of Southwestern Consulting, a Southwestern company, and consists of specialist practices that support clients in every aspect of sales, leadership, and motivation, including keynote speaking and motivational training conferences. Southwestern Publishing House develops and publishes books for leading speakers, corporations, and nonprofit organizations.

Southwestern Consulting:
Tim Nowak, Chief Financial Officer and Senior Partner
Katherine Rowley, Content Manager
sales@southwesternconsulting.com
southwesternconsulting.com | 615-391-2834

Southwestern Publishing House:
Christopher G. Capen, President
Betsy Holt, Publisher
Vicky Shea, Art Director
Kristin Connelly, Managing Editor
Keith Wall, Developmental Editor
Jill Scehovic, Proofreader
swpublishinghouse.com | 800-358-0560

Front cover and interior chapter openers: iStock.com/erhui1979
p. 32: iStock.com/turovsky

I dedicate this book to my wife, Marsha, and to my boys Brayden and Brandon, who are an ongoing source of strength and motivation for me. You have always been behind me and continue to cheer me on to be my best through your amazing love and support.

I also dedicate this book to the thousands of people I have met over the years—and those who I have not—who have overcome tragedy and regained their optimism in life; to anyone who is striving to thrive in life; and to everyone who knows me, hangs out with me, and understands the ups and downs of pushing hard daily. You are my inspiration and motivation for continuing on this sacred path of helping others learn how to perform under pressure.

Contents

Foreword by Major General Robert M. Worley II, United States Air Force (Retired) ... 11

Introduction: A New Look at an Old Issue ... 13

Chapter 1: Say Yes to Stress ... 23

Chapter 2: The Gift of Gravity ... 37

Chapter 3: What Limits Your Performance? ... 47

Chapter 4: A Road Map for Stress Recovery ... 59

Chapter 5: Managing Emotions, Maximizing Energy ... 73

Chapter 6: Preparing for Performance under Pressure ... 81

Chapter 7: Managing the Body and Physical Stress ... 97

Chapter 8: Taming Technostress ... 109

Chapter 9: Creating Inspired Change ... 121

Chapter 10: Cracking Your Personal Stress Code ... 141

Chapter 11: Hope Is the Canvas of Life ... 151

Conclusion: The Beauty of Balance ... 163

Appendix: Macronutrients and Your Health ... 169

Acknowledgments ... 175

Endnotes ... 177

Foreword

BY MAJOR GENERAL ROBERT M. WORLEY II, UNITED STATES AIR FORCE (RETIRED)

The word *stress* conjures up a host of negative thoughts and feelings for most of us. When I hear the word, I am reminded of how I felt in the years following my father's death in combat in Vietnam when I was thirteen years old and later during my time as a cadet at the Air Force Academy. For sure, it was stressful graduating, getting married, and entering the Air Force in a new job. To complicate matters further, my wife and I went through infertility treatment, adopted two children, and raised them through thirteen moves over a thirty-three-year career. During those years, I had some incredibly stressful jobs, many of which involved punishing hours and difficult family separations. These jobs demanded the most from me and from the teams I led. Looking back, I wonder how I managed all the stress.

I also learned the tough lesson that the stress doesn't stop when your children grow up. There are things like colleges, weddings, and grandchildren to keep the stress going. For my wife and me, all of the traditional family life events were punctuated by several difficult periods, beginning in 2012 when my son joined the Marine Corps and went off to war. Having lost my father in war, I couldn't bear the thought of losing my son as well. I suffered many sleepless nights and had to deal with the gravity of this situation each day. Thankfully, he returned safely from Afghanistan. He is still serving, so cultivating emotional and mental health around the situation is an ongoing endeavor.

Then, just one year after my son entered the Marine Corps, my twenty-one-year-old daughter died in a heartbreaking gun accident. Losing my daughter suddenly and tragically has been an experience indescribable in its devastation. Nothing can truly prepare a parent for this. My wife and I both are still figuring out how to live with this reality. We take it a day at a time, but as Dr. Terry Lyles knows, some pain just doesn't go away.

Life is tough. Life is stressful—sometimes very stressful. I don't consider my life story to be any higher on the stress scale than many people who may be reading this. But I do know this: Terry nails it in this book, in terms of how critical our attitude and our actions toward stress are—both in performing at the top of our game and in dealing with life's tragedies.

As a general officer in the Air Force, I called on Terry to coach me and hundreds of my officers and enlisted members at Air Force Space Command and at the Pentagon. He changed our minds about stress and helped transform individuals and organizations into more highly functioning and performing teams. Terry is masterful in bringing together his vast professional experience as a psychologist as well as his own amazing personal life experiences in a powerful delivery that actually changes lives and organizations. I've seen it firsthand.

Performance under Pressure captures the essence of how important stress is and how, with the right understanding and approach to it—including the right mental, emotional, spiritual, and physical perspectives—you can thrive amid the challenges of life.

INTRODUCTION

A New Look at an Old Issue

The island of Phuket, Thailand, is worlds away from the palm-tree-fringed malls and glitter of West Palm Beach, Florida, where I live. Yet when I heard the news on December 26, 2004, I knew I had to go there.

A crack in the ocean floor had opened up, causing a tsunami wave nearly 40 feet high and 180 miles wide (the distance from New York City to Baltimore, Maryland) and traveling at a speed of 500 miles per hour to crash into three continents. Within minutes, the tsunami of 2004 became the largest natural disaster recorded in modern-day history, wiping out hundreds of villages and taking the lives of 175,000 people from Indonesia, India, and Thailand, as well as Christmas vacationers from around the globe.

When news of this disaster reached me, I got up from my desk and walked outside my office. I began contemplating all of the logistics necessary for me to get to the tsunami-torn region to offer my skills in stress recovery training. For more than a decade, I had been helping people cope with trauma and catastrophe. I had witnessed the devastating effects of countless hurricanes in my home state of Florida and elsewhere, as well as the trauma of 9/11 in New York City. As I paced and paced, stunned by the horrific images I'd seen on TV, my phone began to ring. Friends and colleagues wanted to put a plan into action to help the victims of this tragedy. I knew that recovery would be a massive and exhaustive job, but I also knew what I had to offer would be valuable to survivors and rescue workers alike.

I got in contact with my New Jersey business associate and friend Chris Galli, with whom I had done much crisis planning after the 9/11 disaster and in subsequent months training and counseling victims and their families. Chris encouraged me to place my other commitments on hold so I could travel to the far side of the world to offer my services in stress recovery.

I traveled by car, jet, boat, and finally island taxi, winding through the dusty Thai roads, all the way to a scene of unprecedented devastation. I arrived smack-dab in the middle of the most chaotic disaster zone I had encountered to that point. Unlike 9/11, there were no borders to this devastation; it stretched in every direction and as far as my eyes could see. There was a seventy-foot fishing boat lodged between two houses, hotel chandeliers hanging from a twenty-five-foot ceiling now strewn with seaweed, and miles upon miles of debris—everything from clothing to beached, decaying sea life. Worst of all, there was human carnage like nothing I had ever seen.

You can imagine my shock, then, when a Red Cross worker told me that Thailand was doing fine and in need of no assistance. I asked him to repeat himself to make sure we weren't just having a language problem and that I'd heard him correctly. Again, he affirmed that no assistance was needed.

I could only assume by his response that he was in as much shock as the rest of the survivors on this ravaged coast. Flying halfway around the world only to be told that things were "fine" after the worst natural disaster in modern history simply confirmed the need for my work. I knew this man's response, indeed, was a typical stress response—one designed to reassure himself during a difficult time.

I became even more inspired to apply my expertise and experience to help the Thai people. For the next three weeks, I would be working in temperatures approaching one hundred degrees Fahrenheit in the middle of Wat Yan Yao temple, which had been converted into a makeshift mortuary. There, several thousand bodies awaited identification and transportation to grieving families around the world. I would be helping disaster victims and relief personnel learn how to process stress effectively—and how to manage the deep and, at times, paralyzing sorrow and grief that inevitably comes with these situations.

Stress: It's Part of Life

My work in Thailand was one of the most extreme situations I've ever encountered, but it prepared me for my work with trauma survivors and military warriors. A year after the Thailand tsunami, I was called on to assist with the aftermath of Hurricane Katrina. Since then, I've frequently provided guidance to the media, the military, and humanitarian organizations on how to deal with stress effectively during a crisis.

Performance under Pressure: Crack Your Personal Stress Code and Live the Life of Your Dreams is my fourth book on stress. It is the culmination of more than twenty years of work with people of all ages, socioeconomic groups, and nationalities.

We all have one common factor and one wild card factor. Life stress is what we have in common; however, some of us have more than others, depending on circumstances (either in our control or not, as the Asian tsunami illustrates). The wild card factor, what I call the "human factor," relates to our ability (either learned or intrinsic) to not only cope with life stress but also to gain mastery over it.

What does it mean to have mastery over something? Mastery essentially requires two things: *to know and understand* something inside and out, and *to be proficient* with this knowledge through practice and experience. What I aim to accomplish in this book is to give you knowledge—both about stress in general as well as how stress specifically affects you. With this information, you will know how to better handle the pressure in your life. I will also be giving you tools, tips, and exercises that, when practiced consistently, will help you build proficiency and transform your relationship with stress.

There are numerous potential human responses in the face of stress, from simply shutting down one's emotions to exhibiting states of hysteria and catatonia.

Chronic stress has been implicated—either as a cause or for worsening symptoms—in high blood pressure and coronary heart disease as well as autoimmune disorders such as chronic fatigue syndrome and fibromyalgia. It is a factor in diabetes, obesity, anxiety and depression, gastrointestinal problems, asthma, migraines, and Alzheimer's disease.[1]

While natural disasters are some of the most trying events for humans to process, changing social and political environments also cause stress, as do ordinary events over the course of a lifetime, such as getting married, having children, facing deadlines, and changing careers. Even though these are not necessarily crises, they require the same skill set and methods for handling stress. In both cases, support from trained professionals will shorten stress recovery times and pave the way for better outcomes.

After all my years in the field, one thing is certain to me: we are far more capable of handling stress than we think we are. Humans are very resilient.

Let me explain. From the beginning of time, stress has been a part of human existence. We are designed to handle the pressure. Not only are we genetically programmed for it, but in truth, we could not survive without it! When I tell people this, I often see a look of confusion, if not shock, on their faces. Sometimes people say, "Wait, I thought stress was *bad*. Isn't stress something I need to get rid of or at least manage?"

The fact is, stress is not something you can get rid of. It's built into the reality of human existence. Think about the cycle of life: we are born, we grow (and create things like families, careers, friendships, and enterprises), and then we decline and eventually die. Meanwhile, throughout life, we constantly strive for a better existence. This causes us to create all sorts of new inventions, like cell phones, computers, life-saving medical devices, and other technology.

While all of these things can enhance quality of life and solve problems, they also bring complexity and, yes, stress. In fact, invention is *motivated* by stress. Think about it. Most of us no longer experience the stress of having to walk five miles for water because we lack indoor plumbing; the stress of being cold in the winter because there is no heating; the stress of illness due to food spoilage because there is no refrigeration; or the stress of giving birth to a child at home with no medical assistance because there is no hospital or birthing center nearby. So stress is far from "bad." It has been and continues to be a catalyst for better living, and it is an integral part of our creative lives. If you have any doubt about this, ask your mother!

We all know that times change and so do the situations that cause stress. Our ancestors were worried about being chased down and eaten by a tiger. Today's "tigers" are any number of other things, including work pressures, financial hardship, and diseases like addiction, heart disease, and cancer. This is a fact of life on planet Earth: conditions change, but stress is always here.

In addition, technology is creating new pressures in the modern era. One of the key reasons I chose to write this book at this time is to promote awareness of technostress and to assist people in handling the overload related to it. Our unregulated use of and attachment to technology must be explored. As with our consumption of food, we must learn to self-regulate our electronic appetite.

Taking a Different Approach

I hope you can now see how stress is an inherent part of being human in an ever-changing world. I've spent my career educating people about the realities of stress and teaching them how to build a better relationship with it. This is why I'm telling you that *it's fruitless—and a huge waste of time and energy—to try to reduce or get rid of stress.*

The first step in learning to perform under pressure is to realize that you've been taking the wrong approach to stress. Trying to get rid of something that is impossible to eliminate is frustrating at best and disabling at worst. Instead, we need to learn how to see the value of stress and use it to our advantage. In truth, we have been at war with stress for decades now, and this has to stop if we desire real change.

There's more. Not only are we going to stop trying to get rid of stress, but we are also going to make a choice to view stress as *good.* As you will see, perceiving stress as positive is essential to living a longer, more fulfilling life.

Studies abound that demonstrate the effect of thoughts and beliefs on physical and emotional health. As you will read in chapter 8, it is possible to change neural pathways in your brain, essentially creating new "wiring" that causes old thought patterns or behavioral patterns to die out.

Here's the thing I know from working in emergency situations and training athletes and industry leaders over the years: not only are you wired to handle pressure, but *you are also wired for success.* This means it will only take a small adjustment, practiced consistently over time, to break through and begin living a happier and more contented life. With dedication and proper guidance, it is possible for you to finally have the success you want and have been craving for some time.

Medical research supports what I have seen played out over twenty years of working with clients: 75 percent of our longevity[2] is determined by lifestyle choices that include exercise, eating habits, adequate sleep and rest, and how we give and receive love. Most of us know what to do within reason to be healthy, but many of us simply don't do it.

This is why life balance is such an important discussion. As much as it is in our DNA to handle stress well, homeostasis or equilibrium is also firmly rooted in our genes. As organisms on this planet, we are continuously adapting to the external environment and establishing new levels of "normal" (which in terms of human development I often jokingly call "some kind of strange"). The point is, if we overdo technology (or food, or work, or something else) and lose sight of life balance, we will have fallout in some other area of life. It is inevitable.

Much of the content of this book and the title came to me after reflecting upon the chronic nature of our maladaptation to stress. While this might sound scary at first, high levels of stress have occurred throughout history, particularly during times of great leaps in learning. For example, the Industrial Age of the eighteenth and nineteenth centuries created a tremendous shift away from agricultural work and into manufacturing. While the birth of this new age came with stress and pain, the leap forward in terms of the quality of life for humans was remarkable: machines began doing most of our manual labor. I would call this "good stress," which essentially means that we seized an opportunity to create positive change out of a stressful environment.

These shifts are not without repercussions, though. Today, we are facing serious issues as a result of the Industrial Age, including pollution, global warming, food shortages due to drought, natural disasters, and severe human and animal rights violations. All of these challenges, however, are presenting themselves as opportunities in our new technological age to put stress to work for positive change.

Survive or Thrive?

The purpose of this book is to help you make a permanent shift in your relationship with stress so that you can realize new levels of personal health—physically, mentally, spiritually, and emotionally. As this occurs, stress becomes the fuel for creating the no-holds-barred life that most people only dream about. People who have learned to thrive under pressure don't necessarily have less stress than the rest of us; they just see stress differently. They are fully engaged with whatever situation comes up in life, addressing these situations to the best of their ability with openness and full attention. They act and feel alive!

In the pages ahead, we will take a look at the nature of stress and learn to reshape our ideas about it. Just the mere fact that we exist and that we must provide for our own survival and learn how to coexist with others creates pressure. We will explore various aspects of human development that cause stress—and we will also explore tools to help us navigate it.

I want to help you "find your thrive" no matter what circumstances you may be facing. I will teach you how to overcome resistance to stress and how to identify the self-defeating practices that keep you stuck in negative cycles. You will gain information and insight into integrating stress into your life in ways that allow you to move from *survive* to *thrive*. You will also learn valuable tools and practices that will make it easier for you to master your stress on an ongoing basis. Throughout the book, I will share new discoveries and practices for performing under pressure, including stories of people I have worked with as well as experiences from my own life.

If you practice what I'm about to share, you will achieve not only more peace and harmony but also more efficiency and productivity. The happier, more fulfilling life that you seek is within reach. As you will soon discover, anything is possible with stress, including living the life of your dreams.

CHAPTER 1

Say Yes to Stress

"The only difference between a rut and a grave are the dimensions."
Ellen Glasgow, novelist

An essential aspect of thriving under pressure has to do with whether we see stress as good or bad. In reality, it is neither.

Stress, which I also call "gravity," is just a life situation that is asking for our attention and energy. Yes, the gravity of a situation can easily weigh us down, especially in the case of a natural disaster or the loss of a close family member. But as we learn to defy its pull by seeing it as an opportunity for growth, we will come to view stress as good. You may be wondering, "Can stress actually be good for me? And, if so, why is this concept so crucial to living a full and happy life?"

While the phrase *good stress* may sound odd to you (like an oxymoron), I can assure you it is not. I have spent my life and professional career studying how stress can and should be regarded not only as something good but also as an essential ingredient for healthy living.

Before we move on, I want to make sure to clarify one thing. When I say "good stress," I am not at all implying that the events themselves are good. There is nothing favorable about a flood, a sudden death in the family, a car accident, a cancer diagnosis, a shooting, or any number of other horrific circumstances. What I'm saying here is that the stress of the event is what can propel us to new levels of functioning. Yes, we may be broken for a while, but it is the stress, ironically, that will help lift us out of our brokenness.

Most of what we hear about stress today from the media, including scholarly and expert literature, focuses on stress as a dangerous and potentially life-threatening force that must be minimized to ensure good health and longevity. But this is only one side of the story. It's true that unprocessed stress and stress we are not prepared for can be deadly. But here's the good news: *stress that is properly processed is a positive force that helps us learn, move forward in life, and perform with consistency and excellence in any endeavor.*

In the most fundamental sense, stress is our opportunity to practice living fully. As humans, we crave comfort, which means we also tend to hate change—even though life is all about change. So when life comes knocking with what we call a stressful situation, our tendency is to resist it, turn away from it, and maybe even ignore it. Many of us go to great lengths to avoid uncomfortable situations. But that is where the life is! If we turn away from the discomfort (or the "squeeze," as I call it), we miss the chance to learn about ourselves and to make a more positive choice in that moment.

Changing Your View of Stress

My understanding of stress as a potential force for good comes from many years of working with elite performers in sports, business, and the military and with first responders at natural disaster sites. These people view stress differently from most of the population. For example, the stress of competition energizes elite performers in sports and business, spurring them on to consistent and higher levels of excellence. And military personnel and first responders are purposely trained to thrive under pressure. This training taps their reserves of inner strength and discipline and hones their reflexes, physical abilities, and mental processes to such a fine edge that, in the chaos of combat or rescue efforts, they perform with cool precision and unparalleled skill. These people demonstrate on a daily basis that stress can be a powerful and positive force for good.

In reality, stress, competition, and chaos are the same thing—they require the same energy expenditures and draw upon the same resources within us. Ironically, while we view stress and chaos as harmful, we usually regard athletic competitions or rescue missions as positive. This is because most of us don't think of these things, particularly competitive sports, as stress. Yet they are.

Stress is stress, regardless of whether we perceive the circumstances causing the stress as good or bad. Obviously, divorce is stressful, as is the loss of a job or the death of a loved one. But events such as getting married, having a baby, moving to a new home, and receiving a promotion with a big pay raise also inject stress into a person's life, even though these are positive experiences. Unless processed properly, stress and its associated emotions can be harmful, regardless of the circumstances that produced the stress. The key to health and happiness is not necessarily to eliminate the life situation causing the stress; often, this is neither possible nor desirable. But we can regularly process stress and integrate it into our life as a source of inspiration. This is one of the most crucial aspects of performing under pressure: learning to use stress to our advantage to strengthen us and propel us toward greatness.

Understanding how to process and integrate stress is the real key to health and happiness. Anyone with proper training and practice can learn to make stress work for him or her and become a confident and consistent performer, no matter what the situation.

As you apply the strategies presented in this book, you will see how stress can be harnessed to become a powerful, positive force that propels you to personal and/or professional breakthroughs that bring lasting changes. A fuller understanding of the role that stress plays in your life will help you navigate life's storms more easily and successfully. In truth, any of us can be healthy, happy, and prosperous, regardless of how stressful our life circumstances may be.

Stress and Aging . . . or Not

Our ability to cope with and successfully navigate stress affects our life in just about every area. It affects our overall physical health, immediately and over the long term. It affects our capacity to enjoy life, and it has a direct bearing on how long we live. Mental, emotional, and relational issues are also affected by how we handle stress.

As I've mentioned, life is constantly changing; we only need to consider how far technological advances have come in the past thirty years to know the truth of this statement. To be successful in life, we need to embrace the fact that stress (and change) is here to stay. Seeing stress as the enemy will only set us back.

Have you ever wondered why some people age more gracefully than others? Why some people are still going strong into their seventies, eighties, and nineties, while many others grow old before their time? It is generally understood that people with a lifelong habit of caring for their bodies and minds through diet and exercise live longer and enjoy life more than those who don't. Yet another significant factor, and one that is often underestimated, is how well they handle stress on a daily basis.

Having a healthy relationship with stress is important at any age but becomes increasingly so the older we get. Forty-five is the median age where deaths by disease surpass deaths by accidents.[1] If you add poor stress integration to this, the risk of disease becomes higher still. That is why it is so important to learn how to process stress as early in life as possible.

Based on current research and advances, most medical experts believe we should easily be living into our eighties. In reality, while the average life expectancy for Americans has increased to seventy-six for men and eighty-one for women, these figures are deceiving.[2]

Overall, health in America is on a significant decline. We have increasing rates of cancer, heart disease, diabetes, and obesity. Were it not for modern technologies that keep people alive beyond what could be reasonably expected of their bodies, these life span numbers wouldn't be nearly as high. And the problem is not just with adults. The *New England Journal of Medicine* published a report stating that the life expectancy of children of younger generations could be as much as five years shorter due to the obesity epidemic in America.[3]

The difference between ideal and real life spans can be attributed directly and primarily to stress and other lifestyle factors, including what we eat and how active we are (which we will discuss in chapter 7). One thing is for certain: extra weight and other health issues not only increase stress but also affect our ability to deal with stress properly.

The Art of Living Well

Several factors determine how gracefully and slowly we age. Genetics is certainly a major player. Some people simply have the genes for slow and graceful aging. A life of moderation also contributes to health and longevity. By moderation, I mean choosing a lifestyle that avoids tobacco, does not abuse food, alcohol, or drugs (including caffeine), maintains a healthy weight, and includes adequate rest and regular exercise.

The ideal time to learn this philosophy of healthy living is when we are young, although it is never too late to start. To live well and deal with stress, we must understand that our lifestyle choices affect our well-being—physically, mentally, spiritually, and emotionally. If we wish to be healthy, we need to make healthy choices.

It is also important to realize that everything happens for a reason, and while we don't always know what the reason is, we need to trust this principle. If we don't have this mindset, we will likely engage in one battle after another in an attempt to get things to go our way. This creates even more stress, and it works in opposition to what we are learning here. That's not to say that we shouldn't attempt to assert our preferences in life, but we must certainly choose our battles. We need to come to grips with the fact that things don't typically go exactly the way we'd like and that many things cannot be explained, fully understood, or controlled. We like trying to control things, including outcomes. It makes us feel comfortable and confident in the world. But when we control things, we are working in direct opposition to the vulnerability that is required for mastering stress.

Lastly, we must accept the fact that life will not always be easy. The sooner we learn this and the sooner we understand that stress is a natural part of life and can be a powerful, *positive* force, the healthier and happier we will be.

Another key factor in the health and longevity equation is the general ongoing stress level in a person's life. Some careers and professions are high-stress by nature, including the military, law enforcement, firefighting, health-care work (especially emergency-room and trauma-center jobs), teaching, journalism, broadcasting, and professional athletics. So if you are in a high-stress job or find yourself in a stimulating dynamic on a regular basis, you would definitely benefit from a consistent practice for dealing with stress. Regardless of stress levels, however, it is largely our *perception* of stress that can either decrease our life span or extend it.

Before I go any further, I want to note that certain physical health conditions, especially those involving compromised brain health and function, can affect our ability to handle stress. Some people (called "highly sensitive persons" or HSPs) are more sensitive to stress than others and may have more difficulty in processing stimuli. This is also the case for those who suffer from neurological disorders such as autism, Asperger's, and Attention Deficit Hyperactivity Disorder (ADHD). Still others suffer from sports injuries such as concussions or physiological imbalances that can persist into adulthood. These factors can make handling stress more challenging. In these cases, professional support, such as psychotherapy or nutrition and life coaching, can be very helpful. Exercise and other lifestyle enhancements can also make a big difference.

Stress and the Body

As I've noted, whatever its source, stress affects every dimension of our lives: mental, emotional, spiritual, and physical. For example, stress manifests itself in certain physical ways that influence how we respond emotionally to whatever situation that caused the stress. Depending on the stimulus, this physical-emotional interaction can quickly escalate to a dangerous level for someone untrained in proper stress response.

The body responds to a sudden crisis by triggering the release of stress hormones, like cortisol, into the bloodstream. These hormones then stimulate a high-negative emotional response, such as anxiety. This emotion feeds the high physical stress level, and the cycle escalates as the person's anxiety is stimulated to higher and higher levels.[4]

Someone trained in proper stress response will know how to recognize his or her physical and emotional markers, understand the relationship between them, and break the cycle to neutralize the anxiety. As an example, let's suppose that you have been given a deadline that is so tight you are certain it will affect your performance. And let's say you know that this situation is a regular trigger for you—meaning that it causes an extreme emotional reaction. Part of learning to permanently master your stress is to recognize the familiarity of the trigger and have a plan in place for ensuring your success in the situation. With the deadline, you might look for ways to get help on the project or see if you can extend it by a few days. You would then look at this plan and ask yourself if there is any difference between the previous situation and the current one. If the answer is yes, you could modify your plan accordingly, thereby setting yourself up for even more success. If the answer is no, you would need to accept your circumstances and find other ways to manage your stress. (More on that to come.)

So heightened awareness and a willingness to take action when needed are essential for achieving performance under pressure. In addition, ongoing success hinges on the understanding that the process I just outlined is a *practice* that must be consistently undertaken. It is the difference between success and failure in stress navigation.

Call it what you will, but training is what separates the elite from the average. Corporate America spends hundreds of millions of dollars annually, training people to handle whatever on-the-job situations might occur. Training is the lifeblood of the military and professional sports teams, which expend enormous amounts of time, energy, effort, and money turning individuals into elite performers who can navigate high-stress situations.

Familiarity with the key components of training—which include how you think, how you feel, what you believe, and how you respond—will determine your level of proficiency in dealing with challenges in life. As you train, you will be equipped to face difficulties head-on with the intention of winning, which is far different from fearfully avoiding life's challenges and crises.

Fight or Flight

Imagine you are driving down the interstate, enjoying the day, when the car in front of you suddenly stops. You slam on the brakes and swerve to avoid an accident, missing the stalled car by just a few inches. The truck behind you honks loudly. Suddenly, your stress levels are maxed and your heart is pounding.

Nearly all of us have experienced this, and typically we become emotionally triggered. This is called *emotional hijacking*, and it occurs when we feel threatened or endangered. Then our fight-or-flight chemical response is activated.

The fight-or-flight response is natural and important, and it creates physical changes in our body. Whenever our body perceives a threat or danger, it releases stress hormones that increase the heart rate and breathing rate. The body also converts the glycogen stored in the muscles to glucose, providing the muscles throughout our entire body with energy and oxygen for a quick response.[5] With this hormonal release, bodily functions that are not needed in a crisis—such as our digestion, sex drive, and immune system—are suppressed so that all our energy can be focused on the challenge at hand. This entire emergency system serves as a built-in survival and self-defense mechanism.

With the activation of the fight-or-flight response, the person enters a state of heightened awareness in which every sense seems more acute. At

The Fight-or-Flight Response

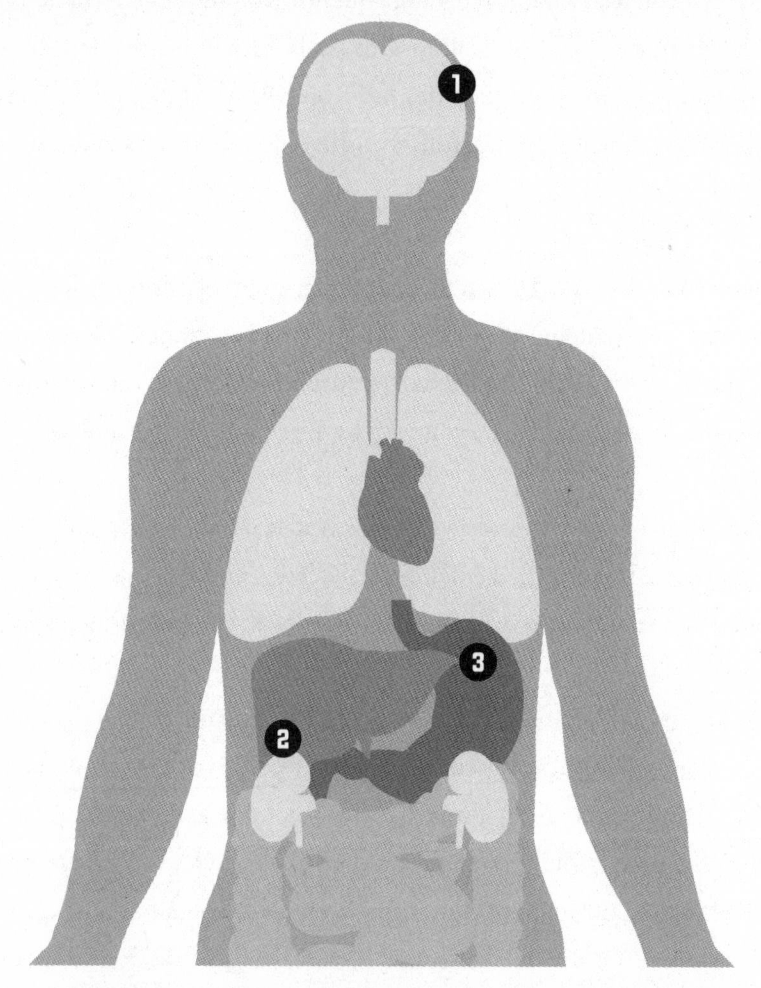

1. Stress causes the sympathetic nervous system to send signals to the adrenal glands.
2. The adrenal glands release stress hormones into the bloodstream.
3. The fight-or-flight response causes a reaction in multiple parts of the body.

first this may be an exhilarating experience, providing a natural chemical "rush," but over the long term, the condition can be deadly. The fight-or-flight chemical response is designed to be active only long enough for us to escape or confront the threat that triggered it. The danger comes when the response continues after the threat has passed or when it is triggered repeatedly by poor response to daily stress.

Because the chemicals released in the fight-or-flight response are toxic in large amounts, this self-defense system is designed to be used only at infrequent intervals and for short periods of time. People who are unable to handle stress set themselves up for increasing health problems, because stress keeps their bodies almost continually in crisis mode. The fire alarm is almost always on, flooding their bodies with potentially dangerous levels of stress hormones. Such a condition can continue for only so long before illness results. People who have received stress-response training or otherwise know how to handle stress well have the ability to turn off the fire-alarm switch more quickly than those who have not been trained.

What happens to the body during prolonged stress? If blood pressure is unregulated during this process, high blood pressure may contribute to blood clotting problems. High levels of cortisol secreted for long periods of time have been linked with diabetes, heart disease, and obesity,[6] in addition to premature aging.[7] Add to this a decreased sex drive and a compromised immune system, and the person's entire mental, emotional, spiritual, and physical capacities are strained.

What I have just described is a picture of growing old fast. So if you want to live a longer, fuller life, you must understand and apply the tools I'm sharing for processing stress efficiently—and do it in a way that works for you. Then stress can be converted into positive energy that will spur you on in life. Gaining mastery over stress means that you have consistent control of your response to stress and, therefore, are not taken on a roller-coaster ride by life's circumstances.

Understanding Your Own Stress Code

We all have a unique stress code—an individual combination of challenges and emotional triggers from our past that affects how we navigate life. To begin to understand your particular stress code and learn how to properly utilize it, you must first evaluate how stress affects you in four primary areas:

- Mentally—your thoughts
- Emotionally—your feelings
- Spiritually—your connection to the "big picture" and your purpose or goal
- Physically—how much energy you have

At any time, you can determine where you are in these four areas and then make necessary adjustments to restore balance. Take some time now to assess where you are today and in your life in general. Feel free to use different colored pens to distinguish between the four zones. Circle your answers to the questions below:

Personal Stress Assessment	1=POOR, 5=EXCELLENT
MENTAL ZONE	
How well can you focus?	1 2 3 4 5
How well are you able to concentrate?	1 2 3 4 5
How well do you handle distractions throughout the day?	1 2 3 4 5
How well do you navigate confusion and indecision?	1 2 3 4 5

EMOTIONAL ZONE	
How well are you managing periods of moodiness?	1 2 3 4 5
How well do you navigate periods of being short-tempered?	1 2 3 4 5
How well do you trust others?	1 2 3 4 5
How well are you dealing with life's stresses overall?	1 2 3 4 5
SPIRITUAL ZONE	
What is your level of personal fulfillment?	1 2 3 4 5
What is your level of professional fulfillment?	1 2 3 4 5
How satisfied are you with your contributions overall?	1 2 3 4 5
How connected are you now to what's most important to you?	1 2 3 4 5
PHYSICAL ZONE	
How would you rate the quality of your energy from morning to evening?	1 2 3 4 5
How would you rate your ability to eat every three hours throughout the day?	1 2 3 4 5
How would you rate your physical conditioning?	1 2 3 4 5
How would you rate your ability to slow down and take rest breaks when needed?	1 2 3 4 5

ADD YOUR ANSWERS TOGETHER FOR A TOTAL SCORE.

75–80: You are operating at peak levels.

65–75: You are operating at above-average levels.

55–65: You are operating below healthy levels.

Below 55: You are in the danger zone, possibly approaching burnout.

Certain types of people can find themselves at higher risk of burnout. For example, it is characteristic of people involved in rescue, relief, and recovery efforts to find themselves in the burnout zone after a disaster; it's also common for emergency room doctors, hospice workers, and other health-care personnel to become drained by the life-and-death nature of their jobs. Other people at risk of burnout include those who have been carrying additional job responsibilities for months or years, those who are living in unhealthy or controlling relationships, and family members who are acting as full-time caregivers. While our mind and body are equipped to handle this level of stress for short periods of time, it can be destructive in the long run if not navigated correctly.

When I train people on how to consistently thrive in life, I ask them to take a daily inventory. When you wake up in the morning, take a few minutes to assess where you are mentally, emotionally, spiritually, and physically. It is important to first understand *where you are*, so you can make choices about *where you want to go* during your day. As you continue through these pages, I will teach you the fundamentals of cracking your own stress code—mastering the daily pressures in your own life so that you can make the changes you want to see.

PERFORMANCE-BOOSTING STRATEGIES

1. Make a decision today to see all stress as good stress. See the stress you encounter in life as an opportunity for growth that will ultimately result in more happiness and success for you.
2. Focusing on what's important—keeping your eye on the prize—is one of the best tools for navigating stress successfully and easily. Take a moment now to write down your vision for your life, your key values, and why you want what you want. Frequently reminding yourself of these priorities strengthens you for those inevitable stresses in life.

CHAPTER 2

The Gift of Gravity

"From birth, man carries the weight of gravity on his shoulders. He is bolted to earth. But man has only to sink beneath the surface and he is free."

Jacques Cousteau, oceanographer and author

The vast majority of people view stress as a bad thing—something to be avoided, ignored, or removed as quickly as possible. That's why I explain that stress is actually a natural and expected part of life for everyone on planet Earth. In fact, stress can be an extremely helpful and positive experience for all of us. To make this point, I use the concept of *gravity* as a metaphor for stress.

Gravity is a law of physics so basic that most of us hardly ever give it a second thought until we fall off a ladder or take a tumble down the stairs. Gravity is one of the four basic forces in nature, along with the strong force, the weak interaction force, and the electromagnetic force. It is the weakest of the forces, yet unlike the others, it has an infinite range.[1] We all know gravity as the attractive force that holds us onto the surface of the earth. Since the earth spins at a velocity of over a thousand miles per hour,[2] without gravity we would all be flung off into space.

Aside from its role in keeping us all literally down to earth, gravity serves another important function: providing us with necessary stress resistance. Gravity is a perfect example of good stress that is woven into the very fabric of nature itself. Whether you realize it or not, we all depend on the stress resistance that gravity provides for our health and survival. Our muscles become strong and conditioned as they continually resist gravity's tendency to pull our body to the ground. Even our heart resists gravity as it pumps blood throughout the body against gravity's tendency to pull all the blood down to our feet. Every moment of our lives is a constant interplay of resistance and balance with the law of gravity.

Gravity as stress resistance is a critical factor to consider in the mission parameters and training regimen of astronauts. When astronauts travel into space, we say they are "weightless" and in a "zero-gravity" environment. Although both of these terms are descriptive, they are not entirely accurate. The force of gravity on an object does weaken in proportion to that object's distance from the source of the gravity, but it never goes away. So there is really no such thing as zero gravity.[3]

Astronauts orbiting the earth are not truly weightless but in a state of perpetual free fall. Gravity is still acting on them and trying to pull them down, but their orbital velocity makes it such that their rate of descent matches the rate at which the surface of the earth curves away below them. They are literally "falling around" the earth.[4]

Prolonged exposure to a "weightless" environment can be devastating to the human body. Over time, the lack of gravitational stress resistance that the body needs to remain strong causes it to atrophy. The muscles (including the heart) and bones weaken, and the mind and emotions also begin to break down. This is why astronauts on long-term space missions, such as those living at the International Space Station, devote a few hours a day to performing specially designed stress-resistance exercises. After returning to Earth, they spend months engaged in specific physical therapy and exercise to restore their bone and muscle mass.[5]

Cooperating with Gravity

In childhood, we all learn how to cooperate with gravity—usually by trial and error. It only takes one or two jumps (or falls) from a bed or a coffee table to learn that the floor is harder than our head. The bumps and bruises and cuts and scrapes of childhood teach us that gravity is a force to be reckoned with.

Orville and Wilbur Wright mastered the secret of controlled, powered flight by learning to cooperate with gravity. Through many experiments—and numerous crashes—the Wright brothers discovered how to achieve the proper balance between gravity and aerodynamic lift. They transformed flight from a wild dream into a practical reality. Once they understood and began to cooperate with gravity, they succeeded in changing the future of transportation forever.

Just as the Wright brothers crashed some planes trying to defy gravity, many of us today are crashing in our personal, relational, and professional lives because we are trying to defy the gravity of a life stress that we have little control over. But like Wilbur and Orville, we can learn to work within the natural laws of that gravitational pull and use gravity to help us soar to new levels of excellence.

Falling forward—essentially, moving through obstacles, seen and unseen—is the first lesson in learning how to work with gravity. Falling forward is a form of inertia that eases us through doors of change and into new opportunities. We are falling forward when we are leaning into success that is not yet seen but only believed in, even if we only believe that things will have to change at some point.

In the case where we are experiencing deep grief, such as the loss of a cherished family member, we may not be able to believe there is anything good for us down the road. The best we may be able to do is to meet our grief compassionately. This, in itself, is a success and a form of falling forward, and over time we may begin to believe that something other than sorrow is possible for us again. This is a great example of working with gravity rather than against it. If we are hard on ourselves about our grief, we will just be creating more stress. So a key behavior in performing under pressure is mentally checking in to see if we are creating more stress for ourselves by resisting the gravity of a situation.

As we go through life, our dreams will likely meet resistance. But utilizing the principle of falling forward, we can convert negative stresses into the life-changing experience of good stress.

Here's just one example of falling forward into success. Several years ago, I was on a weekly flight home and sat next to a businessman. He was downing some prescriptions and having a cocktail to ease his anxiety about the flight. I asked if he was okay, and he replied, "Yes, in about thirty minutes!" He asked what I did for a living, and I said, "I'm a performance specialist." He suggested buying me a drink for a session, and I agreed. We discussed the irrational nature of his fear of flying, since he, the passenger, lacked any control over the outcome. I had him doing real-time visualizations of successful takeoffs and, eventually, a smooth landing to demonstrate that while he could not control the actual mechanics of flight, he *could* control his attitude toward flying.

After talking and laughing for a while, we began discussing how safe air travel really is compared to driving or even being a pedestrian in a large city.

I had him focus on positive beliefs and emotions, which is the key to navigating anything successfully. If we focus on our fears or failures, rather than what we can control in the present moment, we will be miserable throughout any process.

I also asked him if he had ever crashed in an airplane, and he said no. I then asked, "Why are you afraid of the unlikely and low risk of not arriving at our destination?" My goal was to help him realize that the rough, turbulent flight he had experienced years ago was still a safe and successful flight. What's more, his fear was based on the common risk and associated fears that we all face daily by driving, walking, and merely living in an uncertain world. After a few weeks of coaching with me, he came off his medication and began enjoying his in-flight cocktail to relax rather than to escape.

Life is a risk, but not living it moment by moment is an even bigger risk—and tragedy. When we allow ourselves to be consumed by fear, we stop growing, learning, and thriving. In essence, we stop living.

Making Friends with Stress

I've coached elite performers in every field and have carefully watched how they handle pressure. Elite performers do not look at stress as something to be avoided but as a stimulus for continuous improvement and discovery. Instead of pulling back from a challenge, they learn to fall forward and embrace it, knowing that the presence of discomfort or pain does not necessarily mean they have failed or have reached their limit. It may simply mean they have more potential to discover.

For example, top students can memorize hundreds of facts and figures in days, studying long hours to earn excellent grades. The best employees can embrace new corporate philosophies and on-the-job skills, honing these skills even during times of immense stress and change. And seasoned firefighters can operate on little to no sleep during a firestorm, pulling from their mental and physical reserves to finish the job, no matter how daunting.

In short, elite performers learn how to extend their limits. Athletes realize that playing through their pain makes them stronger, builds their character, and helps them achieve and maintain a sharp competitive edge throughout their performance years. At the same time, they learn to recognize where their true limits are so they can avoid hurting themselves.

Training professional and world-class athletes for many years has helped me understand the difference between pain and injury. Pain—whether physical, mental, emotional, or spiritual—is a natural byproduct of growth and development. Pain is just as necessary for growth as good nutrition and sufficient rest. However, it is critical to recognize when we have passed beyond pain into injury. Trying to play through injury is dangerous. It can lead to permanent and even disabling damage. Any type of injury is a signal to stop immediately, get treatment if necessary, and allow sufficient time for healing.

Unfortunately, many of us go through life "playing with injuries," unaware of the serious damage we are causing to ourselves and those around us. We all know the pain of failure, disappointment, disillusionment, betrayal, criticism, and broken relationships. At one time or another, we have all felt emotionally, mentally, or spiritually injured, but learning how to work through this pain—for example, having that difficult conversation, making that therapy appointment, or facing that fear instead of hiding from it—is what makes us stronger, more compassionate human beings.

Understanding the limits of our mental, emotional, spiritual, and physical capacities can actually empower us for growth. The more we learn to "play through the pain" yet stop short of injury, the stronger and more successful we will become.

Balancing Stress with Recovery

Cooperating with gravity's related stress means learning to observe regular cycles of stress and recovery. In sports training, this stress-recovery oscillation is commonly known as *periodization*. Stress recovery can also be referred to as the work/rest cycle. No matter what we call it, though, periodization is the key to building our strength for elite performance in any dimension of life.

The daily stresses of family life and parenthood, especially with a special-needs child who has never been able to walk or speak, helped me learn the importance of balancing work with rest and stress with recovery. Early on in my son Brandon's life, my wife, Marsha, and I spent months visiting with doctors across the United States, frantically searching for a diagnosis with a solution. We were burned out. We were young then, thankfully, and in some ways better able to handle the intense stress and emotions linked to countless sleepless nights and constant dead-ends. But we faced penetrating hopelessness, helplessness, and agony after being told, after months of searching, that nothing could be done for Brandon and that he would not live beyond his teen years. Ironically, this was what catapulted me into action toward a more hopeful future. I'm so glad I didn't give up hope: while Brandon still struggles, today he is thirty-four years old and thriving beyond what anyone predicted.

The fact is, many of our personal and professional problems stem from an imbalance between stress and recovery. Balancing stress and recovery, along with cultivating and maintaining proper perspective, makes the difference between having a positive experience with stress and a negative one.

We've discussed the metaphor of stress as gravity, and I want to describe another essential concept before we go any further: leakage. Gravity leakage is akin to having open portholes on a submarine when it is in dive mode. The gravity of water rushing into a submerging vessel can be costly and very destructive. Therefore, I always begin my coaching process with an evaluation to identify potential leakages.

All compensatory behaviors (whether mental, emotional, spiritual, or physical) are forms of leakage: drugs, drinking, sex addiction, overeating, and so on. Our performance will always suffer if we do not identify and close those portholes properly before plunging beneath the underwater chamber of our daily activity. By developing awareness and accountability tactics in regard to leakage (more on this to come), we can learn to master our stress and maximize our performance.

PERFORMANCE-BOOSTING STRATEGIES

1. Do you have any areas of leakage that you are compensating for with unhealthy activities? If so, what are they?
2. A gravitational pull is anything that requires your attention and energy and has the potential to create stress. What are your gravitational pulls? Some examples are children, family members, work, school, finances, social obligations, technology (including social media), community involvement, personal and family health, and volunteer commitments.
3. Make a list of your gravitational pulls and assign each of them a number from 1 to 10 (10 being a high level of stress). Then ask yourself these questions:
   - What are the benefits I receive from each of these gravitational pulls?
   - How can I reframe the stress associated with these gravitational pulls so that I see them as opportunities for growth (good stress), maximizing my positive experiences with them?
   - Are there any changes that I wish to make?

4. Remember that the gravitational pull of our commitments changes regularly. What you could rate as a 10 in January could drop to a 5 in February, so visit these questions regularly to reorient your mind. This will train you to fall forward into life each day. Finally, see the good in your gravitational pulls. Stress will only weigh you down when you don't see it as a wonderful opportunity to soar.

CHAPTER 3

What Limits Your Performance?

"Don't mistake activity with achievement."
John Wooden, legendary basketball coach

I worked with an Indy 500 driver who would make a pit stop for a quick eight-second service and frequently stall the car, costing valuable time and potential competition results. We discussed the fact that the pits are the most stressful time for a driver, because the control shifts from the driver to the crew working on the car. This alone can be a source of high anxiety for a driver. However, after discussing this further, we uncovered that his fears were actually directly interfering with his ability to keep his attention on the car and to keep it running.

We worked on a new "pit-stop thought" (similar to a "swing thought" in golf) that would alleviate stress so he could remain calm and free from potential performance failures during the stops. We decided on an affirmation of "I've done this a million times," which had an immediate calming effect. After implementing this verbal command along with other emotional navigation tools, such as breathing exercises, my client was able to stay calm in the pits and launch the car back into the race many times without stalling.

This driver's situation applies to many people. If we merely listen to our thoughts as they pass through, versus directing the conversation we have with ourselves in affirming commands, we will accumulate mental stress and pain, which interferes with performance.

Since performance is key to one's ability to thrive in life, it makes sense to have some understanding of where you perform well in life and where you do not. Let's do an exercise. Study the list below and identify as many performance-limiting characteristics that you feel apply to you. If there is a characteristic that you really struggle with that is not listed here, include it. Take your time and be honest with yourself. Remember, performance-limiting characteristics cause stress. So in order to make progress, we will slowly convert these energy-draining behaviors into energy-producing behaviors.

Performance-Limiting Characteristics (circle any that apply):

- Poor team player
- Low energy levels
- Poor follow-through
- Poor time management
- Low motivation
- Poor leadership
- Negative thinking
- Negative self-talk
- Poor fitness
- Poor diet
- Chronic fatigue
- Poor work-life balance
- Strained relationships
- Mental/physical inflexibility

- Insensitivity to others
- Short temper
- Poor sleep habits (a.m. fatigue)
- Fear or paranoia
- Lack of trust in self/others
- Lack of life inspiration
- Lack of patience
- Lack of adequate rest/breaks throughout the day
- Too concerned about others and not enough attention on self
- Know-it-all syndrome
- Unclear purpose

What things are you really dealing with in life? What habits, characteristics, or behaviors limit your performance? Identify as many as necessary. From your initial list, choose the three that consistently interfere with high performance:

- ____
- ____
- ____

From those, choose one behavior to begin your journey. Generally, we are more successful in effecting change when we keep a sharp and narrow focus. If we try to juggle too many things at once, we will probably drop all of them and give up in discouragement. That's the reasoning behind starting with one item.

An old proverb says that the way to build a house is one brick at a time. Begin with one behavior and concentrate on it exclusively, using the techniques described in the rest of this chapter over the next thirty to forty-five days (or until you get it down). If you require a coach to help you in any particular area, get one; this will help you find clarity on what changes are needed and give you some built-in support for making them.

Partnering with an expert shortens the learning curve and helps you recover from missteps more quickly. Also, keep in mind that some changes have multiple phases or layers, which a professional can help you identify. After concentrating on one item, move to item number two and do the same thing. Follow up with item three. It will take anywhere from three to five months to complete the changes in these three areas. This is not necessarily a fast process, but when you approach it this way, your changes will be more successful and permanent.

Results can vary, but according to research, it can take an average of two months to create a new habit.[1] Start with thirty to forty-five days and see what works best for you. This will allow sufficient time for the new habits or behaviors to get loaded into the autonomic nervous system where, under a subconscious triggering mechanism, they will become second nature.

Prepare Your Action Plan

Identifying and targeting a specific goal for change and improvement is important, but to ensure success, you need an action plan—a system to follow every day during the thirty- to forty-five-day period. Notice that some of the elements of the plan are items we have discussed earlier. This is deliberate, because all of these things are interconnected.

Daily Life Navigation System

1. *Start each day with "purpose alignment."* This is pretty simple. Each morning, at the beginning of your day, take two to five minutes—longer if needed—to align yourself by identifying what is most

important for you that day and in your life overall. Zero in on that bull's-eye from which your passion, motivation, perseverance, and force flow.

2. *Rest and recover every ninety minutes.* This element is too important to ignore. Don't bypass this step; you will only shortchange yourself and frustrate your goals in the long run. (There will be more information on rest and recovery in chapter 4.)
3. *Journal your daily progress.* Take time each evening to assess your progress during the day by rating yourself (low, average, or high) in the areas of purpose, nutrition, exercise, energy, and recovery. How did you do in each area throughout the day? Are you on track, or is there some area that needs more attention? Were you passionate in your purpose today? Did you make wise choices for your meals and snacks? Did you exercise today? How were your energy levels? Did you take any recovery breaks?

The next page includes a chart I use in training to help with daily journaling. Use it to track your progress and keep an ongoing record for day-by-day comparison. This will help you see where you are improving, where you may be stalled, or where you may be falling back. It will also give you an idea of where stress may be creeping into your day without your awareness.

Coaching Accountability Chart					
RATING SCALE: 1=LOW, 2=AVERAGE, 3=HIGH					
WEEK	PURPOSE	NUTRITION	EXERCISE	ENERGY	RECOVERY
Sunday					
Monday					
Tuesday					
Wednesday					
Thursday					
Friday					
Saturday					

As I mentioned earlier, find someone you trust and respect who will agree to be your coach, or at least hold you accountable from day to day and week to week. We need accountability to help us stay focused on our goal. Implementing change is always easier when there is someone encouraging and cheering us on from the sidelines.

Training Makes the Difference

Remember, chaos, stress, gravity, and life storms (i.e., heavier gravity that affects our lives for some time) are normal parts of life. We will never completely escape life's challenges. With proper training, however, we can navigate them successfully and prosper from them, thriving even under significant pressure.

Early in my psychology training, I interned for two years as a crisis phone counselor in Detroit, Michigan. During my first week, I fielded three suicide calls. One of the callers told me he had a gun pointed to his head and was going to pull the trigger unless I could say something that would help him.

Thank God for good training! My first response from training was to use some humor to break his focus on self-inflicting bodily harm. I said, "Please don't pull that trigger, because I don't want the sound ringing in my ear."

After a moment of silence during which the caller processed my comment, he snickered and asked, "Are you crazy?"

"Not today," I replied, "but I can relate to how you feel."

My unexpected response changed his focus long enough to allow me to connect with him and effectively communicate that other people cared about him. We spoke for quite a while, and in the meantime, the crisis center followed emergency protocol and deployed a first response team to his home to assist him.

After the phone call ended and I came to my senses, I realized how close I had come to witnessing a suicide during my watch. My next thought was how well I had been trained to function in chaos and how to not panic, instead trusting my training instincts to help me reach out with compassion and render assistance.

Since that early training experience, I have learned to thrive in chaos, knowing that chaos is only a temporary transition to a more permanent station in life. Chaos is inevitable, but with proper training and focus, we can move through it with courage rather than fear. This courage will enable us to charge like a warrior into harm's way, making progress in order to make a difference.

Pastor and author Charles Swindoll famously said, "I am convinced that life is 10 percent what happens to me and 90 percent of how I react to it." After decades of coaching and working with clients, I wholeheartedly agree. We all have the full potential and opportunity to grow in a healthy way and respond well to the most challenging events of our lives. Think for a moment. What life experiences have made you the toughest and strongest? Were they not the periods of your greatest struggles and difficulties? Learning to process stress and make it work for us is a powerful tool that will help us become well-rounded and highly gifted individuals, able to deliver consistently high performance in any situation.

The Importance of Coaching

As I've said before, if we are to truly break through from what is limiting our performance, we need coaches or mentors. Good coaches will help us identify our sources of leakage and encourage us to keep pushing forward when we encounter stress.

If you're still not sure, consider this:

1. *The best athletes and performers in the world have coaches.* Some people might say, "I don't need any help, I don't need any accountability in my life, and I don't need a coach. I know what I need to do." Self-reliance is one thing, but this attitude is a recipe for failure. Actors employ dance teachers, trainers, dialect coaches, and other experts to get ready for their next big film. Singers like Carrie Underwood and Tim McGraw have voice coaches. And athletes like Tom Brady and LeBron James have football and basketball coaches.

   Not only do the best athletes and performers in the world have coaches, they recognize better than anyone else that they *need* coaches. That is one of the reasons why they are the best in the world: they never stop learning, and they never stop trying to improve.

In fact, I can say—as someone who trains a wide range of people, from families to corporations, professional athletes to members of the military—that none of us should ever stop learning, for the one reason called inertia. When we stop learning, we lose momentum in life; we atrophy—mentally, emotionally, spiritually, and physically. Peak performers are always striving to learn more and to get better at what they do. They constantly compete against themselves, seeking always to run a little faster, jump a little higher, and advance a little further than last time.

2. *If we are in the game, we cannot see the game!* This is another reason coaches are important. When we are right in the thick of things, it is hard, if not impossible, to maintain a balanced view of the situation or our own capabilities. We need someone to help us who has a visual-spatial perspective on what is happening. That is what a coach provides.
3. *We will not consistently outperform our training.* In other words, we must train in the same way we expect to play or perform. We can't continually blow off study and preparation and expect to do well. As a general rule, our performance will be only as effective as our training. We should set our sights high and train with the goal in view.

Broadway performers are notorious for their hard work, but it pays off with many stunning performances on stage. Top athletes, whether amateur or professional, put in long, demanding hours in training that spectators rarely see, just so they can shine for a few minutes with an over-the-top performance in their chosen sport. The well-known adage is true: "No pain, no gain." Training that pushes us to our edge is critical for peak performance.

4. *A minimum thirty-day commitment with tough coaching is necessary to make changes and keep them a reality.* Any permanent change in our life requires at least thirty days (some studies show sixty days) to take hold. If, for instance, we want to institute a balanced nutrition and exercise program, we will need to follow it consistently in order for it to become part of us.

Changing our habits or lifestyle is a push-pull cycle. Until we have practiced the change or new discipline consistently, it will be a "push" for us. We will have to fight to maintain the change, because old habits die hard. If we are used to staying in bed a few extra minutes in the morning, we will have to push ourselves to get up early enough for the two-mile run that we have committed to. If we have a frequent strong hankering for pizza, we will have to push ourselves to opt for a salad instead.

After we have practiced the change consistently, a transition will occur where the push becomes a "pull," and we find ourselves drawn to the new behavior instead of the old. We will feel pulled to work out and pulled to eat that salad, because we have experienced the benefits of a healthy lifestyle. Building systematic change into our lives by sticking with it long enough to get from "push" to "pull" is easier when we align the desired changes with our life purpose. If we know *why* the change is important, the inspiration and motivation to make it happen are easier to find.

PERFORMANCE-BOOSTING STRATEGIES

1. Most of us have had the experience of starting a new ritual we think is positive, only to not follow through. Take a moment to reflect on a recent ritual that you started and then stopped. It could be related to diet, work, exercise, or a way of communicating with

your spouse. See if you can identify what stopped you from following through.

2. Next, write down five specific actions that could have helped you stay with that commitment. (Note: this could include support from others.)
3. Take a moment to visualize achieving that goal: How would you look and feel? How would your life look and feel? Then ask yourself, "Do I really want this change (meaning is it internally or externally motivated)?"
4. Determine which of the five specific actions you are willing to start taking today to get back on track.

CHAPTER 4

A Road Map for Stress Recovery

"No one can get inner peace by pouncing on it."
Harry Emerson Fosdick, Protestant minister

Every day I was in Thailand after the Asian tsunami, I drove ninety minutes each way to the most devastated area of the country, near the city of Khao Lak in the Phang Nga province. The drive off the main road into the village areas always shocked me. As I surveyed the devastation each day, I imagined the screams, horror, and chaos of that awful morning.

This area had sustained the most damage because a coral reef near the shoreline pushed the tsunami wave higher than anywhere else in Thailand. A wall of thundering water more than forty feet high had rushed almost two miles inland, wiping out everything in its path. Local families and tourists were caught off guard and tried to outrun the massive wave. Thousands of people lost their homes and possessions as well as family members and friends.

I drove until I saw families gathered in an effort to make it through another day. My jeep was loaded with food, toys, medicine, first-aid supplies, and soft drinks, which were a big hit with the kids. The supply containers I handed out always brought smiles of delight and tears of gratitude. As I shared a few moments of common humanity with these Thai families from Khao Lak, barriers of ethnicity and nationality dropped. A bit of hopefulness refilled each person's "cup," and we all seemed to put a few coins in one another's "inspiration meter."

Each evening, I drove back to the base camp in Phuket to restock my supplies for the following day. I did so with mixed emotions, feeling stressed and conflicted at having to leave those wonderful people for even one night. What an awesome opportunity it was to go in day after day, offering food, care, and counseling to those families and relief workers. I was inspired by their courage, good spirit, determination, and, most of all, by the renewing of their emotional and physical energy as they experienced genuine hope for recovery and a return to normalcy.

In the midst of the direst of circumstances, just choosing to believe that things will eventually be okay is sometimes all we need to move forward. Such is the awesome power of good stress. When we become proficient in the practice of seeing stress differently, eventually that becomes our way of living and being in the world. Stress, properly seen, understood, and utilized, can ignite the fire of growth and change necessary not only for survival, but also for thriving in life. At the same time, understanding the role of emotions and energy is key to maximizing the vibrancy and vigor of youth throughout our lifetime. When we know how to recharge effectively from stress, we are able to make the paradigm shift to viewing stress as positive rather than negative.

Every day, we create and expend energy. Our bodies need frequent deposits of energy in order to navigate through daily stresses, especially in times of extreme duress. If we don't manage our deposits and expenditures of energy well, we'll find ourselves "in the red." Having optimal health and performance requires careful attention to the stress/recovery cycle, also known as the work/rest cycle. Without sufficient rest, we may suffer a physical, mental, emotional, or spiritual crash.

Take Time to Recover

When we sleep, our body goes through a ninety-minute cycle in which the brain moves from more alert to less alert. Many researchers believe this rhythm also occurs during our waking hours[1] as part of an "ultradian rhythm." I have followed this research for many years and firmly believe that because of our body's natural cycle, we require brief recovery periods every 90 to 120 minutes throughout the day. I refer to this exercise of taking breaks as *oscillation*. This means movement back and forth, and it requires us to move our bodies and change our focus. This regular oscillation throughout the day is in addition to the high-quality sleep we need each night to replenish our energy reserves.

A daily recovery strategy does not need to be complicated or time-consuming: we're talking about a two- to five-minute recovery break after every 90 to 120 minutes of work. This simple practice will put you light-years ahead of the majority of people living and working in our modern world. Things like taking a walk around the block, sharing a joke with a coworker, or taking a few moments to stand up, stretch, and breathe will help to maintain your energy levels and concentration throughout the day.

Many of us handle our workday in a linear fashion: we start work at a dead run and charge straight through the day without stopping, sometimes not even for lunch. A graph of that approach would show a straight line, which bears an alarming resemblance to a flatline on an EKG or EEG machine. (And make no mistake—if your EKG or EEG flatlines, you are having a very bad day!) On the other hand, the graph of a healthy stress/recovery cycle would show an up-and-down movement, like a healthy EKG pattern. This is how we are actually designed to function.

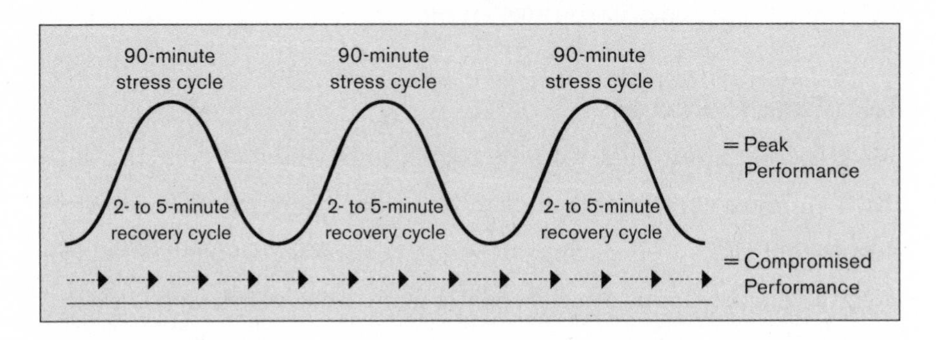

But how we are *designed* to function is an entirely different issue from how we are *programmed* to function. Most of us are programmed by our culture, society, and our employer to take breaks only when absolutely necessary, instead of when it is absolutely optimal. This results in a drop in productivity and performance quality as the day progresses.

How, then, do we go about changing our external work habits to allow for daily oscillation, which leads to better stress navigation? Each of us must take charge of our own energy-recharging system. We all have the ability to focus, concentrate, and emote in a positive direction. Our mind and emotions need as much recharging as our body requires—and with equal frequency. Sometimes we talk about the four dimensions of our person—mental, emotional, spiritual, and physical—as if they were separate and distinct. But in reality, the function of one affects the function of the others. We need all four dimensions to be recharged on a regular basis if we are to run consistently on all cylinders. This helps us to not only achieve peak performance but also to maintain daily balance, which ultimately leads to greater fulfillment and contentment in life.

The energy we need to recharge our system every day is abundantly available through nourishing food, exercise, adequate sleep, and recovery time. If we find ourselves consistently running an energy deficit, wearing out before the end of the day, the problem may have nothing to do with an energy shortage—the problem may be with how we build up, transport, and deliver energy to our system as needed. And we do this through a daily cycle of eating, sleeping, resting, exercising, and recovering.

Developing an abundance mindset—believing that there's plenty of energy available *and* that we have the ability to recharge throughout the day—will transform the way we think and act. Many of the people I've coached who thought they had exhausted their resources found they actually had abundant resources of energy for working hard, playing hard, and enjoying life to the fullest. Once they learned how to tap into these energy sources, they no longer needed to worry about running out of energy. Instead, they realized they had all the energy required to meet the regular demands of the day, as well as a deep reserve from which to draw when an extra push was required.

I like to compare our daily cycle of stress and recovery to high-speed auto racing. Indy and Formula 1 (F1) car drivers, for example, compete for several hours at speeds over 200 mph. To save on weight and to increase efficiency and safety, these cars have small fuel tanks. This means they can complete only a few laps at a time before they must make a quick pit stop.

A normal pit stop lasts three to seven seconds. In this short flash of time, tires are changed, the fuel tank is filled, and the visor is cleaned. Any other necessary adjustments are made to prepare the car for its next performance cycle. Missing a pit stop immediately degrades the car's performance, sometimes disastrously. The car may run out of fuel, or the engine may break down, or a tire may fail, with potentially catastrophic results.

Similar to race cars, our bodies also have a small fuel tank and can carry us at peak performance for only about 90 to 120 minutes before we need a pit stop to refuel and recharge. After two hours, our performance begins to drop off drastically. So we need a two- to five-minute pit stop to energize us fully for the next 90- to 120-minute rotation. When we implement this simple technique of building regular rest/recovery periods into our day to manage stress, we will notice a significant difference in our performance.[2]

In addition to providing immediate health benefits, this approach shows us how well we can perform and how far we can go during a normal rotation. It also shows us how much "afterburner energy boost" we have for dealing with a crisis. In other words, we learn what our limits are and how far we can surpass those limits when necessary. Knowledge of this can help us avoid pushing ourselves too far, risking injury or damaging our health.

By respecting our stress and recovery cycles and moving between them throughout the day, we build and sustain our physiological and emotional momentum, which leads to peak performance and productivity. This applies to children as well as adults, because all of us are performing daily, be it as an executive, coworker, sibling, parent, spouse, or friend.

Getting in Tune with Nature

Have you ever noticed how much energy children have, running and bouncing around every single day? The reason is simple: children are more connected to their natural cycles than we grown-ups are to ours. Consider how often infants need to recharge their batteries. They eat every two to three hours, sleep for several hours, and are awake for several hours. That is their natural daily cycle.

As adults, we have lost touch with our own internal rhythms. The demands of school and then the workplace have conditioned us to believe in and adhere to an unnatural cycle in which we are expected to work, study, and perform for hours on end, without rest. But we can learn the value of respecting our natural cycles, both for our health and to ensure peak performance under pressure.

As adults, we need less sleep than infants and adolescents because we don't have the same physical developmental needs. Adults require seven to nine hours of sleep daily for physical recovery.[3] Even with quality sleep, however, we still need regular and frequent rest breaks. Otherwise, our energy levels will diminish.

Another thing that prevents us from getting in touch with our natural internal cycles is our strongly acculturated habit of eating three meals a day. Expert opinions about diet and exercise vary widely, but my twenty-plus years as a performance coach has taught me that we manage stress and perform best when we eat small portions of healthy food every three hours. Of course, meals need to be smaller in size than what most of us are accustomed to—an appropriate balance of complex carbohydrates and proteins interspersed with "power snacks" of around 250 calories. While it is a challenge to eat smaller portions in our supersize-me culture, it *is* possible.

Along with proper nutrition, we need adequate exercise. Most working Americans spend their days behind a desk with little need to move around in order to do their jobs. While it may not be practical or possible to get a full exercise workout in the office, it's easy to get several brief periods of movement during the day. After ninety minutes of sitting at a desk, our bodies begin signaling to us that we need to move around. If we ignore these signals and fail to move around, our concentration and emotional faculties begin to wane.

Stand up. Stretch. Go get a drink of water. Hand-carry a memo instead of using the phone or email. Use the stairs instead of the elevator, or park farther away from the building. Walk to lunch. Do anything to put some movement into your routine. We need to bring our exercise and eating habits into alignment with the internal rhythm of our natural stress-recovery cycle.

Sleep Versus Rest

The inventor and scientist Leonardo da Vinci said, "Every now and then go away, have a little relaxation, for when you come back to your work your judgment will be surer."

If energy is the fuel that we run on, then rest is the gas station where we fill our tanks back up. I believe there is a difference between sleep and rest. Sleep is *physical* and rest is *spiritual*. This distinction is a crucial one. Sleep is physical because it's something we need in order to recover a portion of our energy, as well as to repair the wear and tear to the body that happens during the day. But we do not get all of our replenishment from the sleep cycle.

Rest is an equally necessary form of recovery. I call it our internal "peacemaking process." Rest provides a needed respite in the midst of daily activity. It nourishes us in an equally essential way as sleep does. Learning to incorporate both rest and sleep into our lives will make the difference we've been looking for in sustainable energy.

Neglecting our need for regular periods of rest throughout the day is another example of how we work against our basic wiring. Part of what is so vital about rest is the role it plays in our ability to recover from the daily stresses of life. As I've said before, gravity/stress itself isn't the problem; rather, it is our response to it that determines our energy level. Lack of recovery is the main reason so many of us have trouble coping with the demands of today's fast-paced world. Society—including corporate America—has programmed us to believe that more and faster are always better, but that is not true.

The most consistently productive people are the ones who learn how to keep refueling their engines throughout the day with proper eating, hydration, exercise, and rest cycles. For example, Kevin Cleary, CEO of Clif Bar, regularly runs twenty miles a week and aims to be home every night by 6:30 to be with his family. He also coaches his children's sports teams and logs eight hours of sleep each night. Media mogul Oprah Winfrey makes an effort to meditate once or twice a day for twenty minutes.

Rest gets a bad rap among people who think it's a form of laziness or an ineffective use of time. In reality, rest is natural and productive. When you take care of yourself, you probably notice you respond better to stress. When you're pushing yourself in one or more areas of your life, your response to stress takes more out of you.

How fast is your speed of recovery? Think about the four cylinders you run on: mental, emotional, spiritual, and physical. Mentally, when you get distracted, how long does it take you to get back to what you were doing? Emotionally, when you're angry or upset, how quickly can you get back to a neutral or even a happy state? Spiritually, how soon can you get back in touch with your belief system and your core self when they are challenged? Physically, how quickly can you recover after you've lost energy? And, in all of these cases, how healthy is that recovery strategy? Smoking a cigarette may help you recover quickly from a moment of stress, but it's not healthy.

Infants and toddlers recover almost immediately from stress because they know how to recover. They haven't learned anything different! They sleep or they cry or they zone out or they ask for something to eat. They don't suppress their body's needs or their emotions. Ultimately, by tuning back into your natural rhythms, you'll respond to stress much more effectively. Rest is an essential tool in that arsenal.

Acknowledging your need to recover helps get you back in touch with your natural rhythms, which propel you forward in your day and in life.

You are going to be more productive and create more positive momentum by resting properly. Stress will always be there, so by making regular recovery a priority, you are ensuring you will be able to consistently perform under pressure.

Rest Is Spiritual

How often do we need periods of rest? Studies show that ninety minutes is the optimal peak performance window; two hours is the maximum.[4]

Sports games and theatrical performances follow this natural law. Football, basketball, hockey, and softball are punctuated by periodic breaks: time-outs, quarters, and halftimes. And most plays include a twenty-minute intermission after the first act, which lasts about ninety minutes. The actors recover so they can refuel and return to the show with renewed energy. Without such periods of rest, even the best actors and athletes would see their performance suffer.

We're the same, even if we're not running down a tennis court, singing or acting on Broadway, or rounding the bases. It doesn't matter what we're doing, whether we are working or playing, whether we're active or inactive. Without recovery, our mental, emotional, spiritual, and physical acuities drop dramatically after two hours.

In other words, we need a mini-vacation several times a day. How's that for good news? But what exactly does that mean? We should push the envelope and work as hard as we can for 90 to 120 minutes and then oscillate—take a break and repeat. Eventually, your day will look like the wavy line of activity and recovery in regular 90- to 120-minute cycles (like the graph that was depicted earlier in the chapter).

In fact, I lay out my day in ninety-minute segments and find it is so much easier (and productive) to deal with what the day brings by utilizing these intervals. If I've been working at my computer for most of the day, I might get up and stretch after ninety minutes. If I've been walking around a conference center, I might find a secluded bench where I can sit and call home.

Your break can be anything: meditate, go outside, stretch your arms above your head, get a drink of water, or listen to some music. Just do something that breaks one cycle of activity and prepares you for the next. That break will reinfuse you mentally, emotionally, spiritually, and physically, *if* you have the right recovery strategy, which is different for everyone. So, you may have to play around with it a bit to figure out what works best for you. If you don't know what that might be, list some brief activities you like and then start experimenting. You will quickly discover the best options for you. The key is taking these breaks regularly.

Sleep Is Physical

In addition to neglecting our need for periodic rest throughout the day, most Americans do not get enough sleep. According to Gallup, the average American clocks in just 6.8 hours each night.[5] Sleep regulates every aspect of our being—mood, immune function, memory, metabolism, and virtually every other imaginable process. As a result, sleep deprivation hinders our ability to respond to stress effectively and perform under pressure. Many people become so accustomed to poor sleeping habits that they don't realize sleep deprivation is causing them difficulties in multiple areas of life.

Sleep is a component of our basic wiring. It's important that we learn to work with it rather than against it. We need to literally "power down" from the activity of the day before we go to bed, just like a computer does before it sleeps. People tend to think their sleep problems are the result of stress, psychological or otherwise, and they might just be. But more often than we might expect, it is the seemingly trivial things we do before we go to sleep that set us up for unrestful sleep.

In many cases, a good sleep routine can resolve many seemingly chronic sleep problems. Because of the body's natural rhythms, it responds well to sleep routines. The more rituals we can build into our sleep pattern, the better.

Here are some tips:

- *Go to bed at the same time every night and wake up at the same time every morning.* Your body will rapidly adjust to this routine, and you'll find it easier to fall asleep and wake up.
- *Limit stimuli thirty minutes before bedtime.* This means no television (especially the evening news, which is highly anxiety-provoking), no deep conversations at home or on the telephone, no scrolling through social media, no checking your email or texts, and no strenuous physical activity. If you like to read, limit it to something light and enjoyable that will help you relax.
- *Don't eat ninety minutes before bedtime, since your digestion will interfere with falling and/or staying asleep.* Avoid caffeine (including chocolate) after lunchtime if you think it might be interfering with your sleep. Studies have found that caffeine can take four to six hours to metabolize.[6] Sleep, not coffee or soda, should be fueling you.
- *Sleep in a dark, cool room.* Eliminate light as much as possible, whether outside or inside. Invest in room-darkening shades if you get up after dawn or are bombarded by street lighting.
- *If you wake up in the middle of the night, don't look at the clock!* Learning the time will only put your brain into analytical mode and trigger anxiety,[7] making you less likely to attain quality rest.
- *Don't hit the snooze button.* Most psychologists and sleep scientists

agree that it's better to set your alarm for the last possible minute you need to wake up. You'll get better quality rest by sleeping all the way through instead of interrupting your sleep cycle with a nine-minute snooze button.[8] So get up, turn on the lights, and start your day.

PERFORMANCE-BOOSTING STRATEGIES

1. List ten healthy things that you can do for rest and recovery that take ten minutes or less. Some examples: calling a friend, deep breathing, stretching, movement or exercise, visualization, meditation, prayer, reading a chapter in a book or a magazine article, writing a card or note, or playing with a pet.
2. Monitor your new oscillation cycles in 90- to 120-minute periods and take two- to five-minute breaks to recharge and restore your energy levels.
3. If need be, program your computer with reminders or set a timer. Do this for at least thirty days in a row, and you will be compiling a lifelong annuity that pays big benefits.

CHAPTER 5

Managing Emotions, Maximizing Energy

"Let's not forget that the little emotions are the great captains of our lives, and we obey them without realizing it."
Vincent van Gogh, artist

Emotions and physical energy are interconnected and inseparable, a true force to reconnect with daily. Still, we all know that managing emotions is not easy, and we are often emotionally hijacked by ourselves or someone else. Without the tools and skills to navigate these challenging situations, we'll find ourselves confused and unable to perform at a high level. So, learning to control emotions and energy levels is essential to performing well under pressure.

If you've ever had a terrible experience with customer service—such as waiting on hold for an hour, only to be dropped from the call as soon as the representative comes on the line—you know exactly what I am talking about. Your emotional fire alarm may be activated. If not deactivated properly within thirty seconds or so, you may be tempted to act on your red-hot emotions and energy levels. No good will come of that!

Human emotions and the physical energy linked to these emotions are constantly changing. At any given moment, we may operate from either a high or low energy level with a corresponding emotional state. High energy is linked with an excited, pumped, and challenged emotional state, while low energy is connected with fear, frustration, and exhaustion.

A person in a high-emotion/high-energy state has a bounce in her step and high spirits. Her face and body language mirror that high energy level. Likewise, someone who is tired will express it in his actions, moping and dragging, for example.

The word *emotion* literally means "to move, to set in motion" or to start movement of any kind.[1] Emotions are the gauges that tell us that we are alive. The issue of stress is not with the emotions themselves, but instead with learning how to understand and navigate them. We do this first by identifying the energy level or emotional quadrant we are operating from (high or low, positive or negative) and then using that knowledge to make the transition from how we are feeling to how we would prefer to be feeling.

The Emotional Navigram

Dealing with emotions can be tricky. The following chart, or "navigram," helps us visualize how all our emotions relate to each other. I call this chart a navigram because it aids in navigating our emotional and energy states.

The Emotional Navigram	
HIGH NEGATIVE **(Negative emotions/high energy)**	**HIGH POSITIVE** **(Positive emotions/high energy)**
Angry Fearful Frustrated Anxious	Excited Connected Challenged "Pumped"
LOW NEGATIVE **(Negative emotions/low energy)**	**LOW POSITIVE** **(Positive emotions/low energy)**
Sad Depressed Lonely Exhausted	Calm Peaceful Relaxed Recharged

The navigram classifies emotions according to energy levels and locates each in a particular quadrant. The two quadrants on the right contain positive energy and emotions, while the two on the left contain negative energy and emotions. The upper-right high-positive quadrant contains positive emotions with a high-energy output—excited, connected, challenged, and "pumped." Below it is the low-positive quadrant of positive emotions with a low-energy output—calm, peaceful, relaxed, and recharged.

The low-negative quadrant contains low energy and negative emotions such as sad, depressed, lonely, and exhausted. The upper-left high-negative quadrant contains high-negative energy and emotions such as angry, fearful, frustrated, and anxious.

Emotionally, we are constantly moving between quadrants. Sometimes an event happens that drags us from one quadrant to another, while other times we make choices that move us around. Someone may cause us to feel angry, propelling us into the high-negative quadrant, but staying there is a choice we make. Remember the example that I used earlier in the chapter about being on hold for an hour and then getting disconnected as soon as you've gotten a customer service agent on the line? This kind of incident happens to all of us, but how we navigate this common experience is the key to emotional stability. Remember to take two to three deep breaths—or to try other stress techniques such as the ones presented later in this chapter. Doing so will regulate the chemical response to emotional hijacking and help you respond positively within twenty to thirty seconds, restoring some calmness and resulting in a more civilized phone call.

Our circumstances may cause frustration, but how we choose to navigate them makes all the difference. Choosing between anger, sadness, excitement, calmness, and joy is up to us.

In my own life and coaching practice, I follow a "90/10 rule"—I believe that 90 percent of reality is perception while 10 percent is unchangeable. I see many people get stuck in a negative emotional quadrant because they don't know how to navigate out of it or because they spend 90 percent of their time trying to change the 10 percent of reality that will not change. But gravity is always in force. The sun always rises in the east and sets in the west. These are unchanging realities.

A secret to navigating our emotions is identifying what is changeable and what is not. We need to identify those things that are within our power to change and learn to let go of those things that are outside our reach. It is not what happens to us in life that defines us, but rather how we respond to what happens to us. For example, we can control how we decide to set boundaries or take care of ourselves—but we can't control what people are going to think about us or whether they are going to get mad when we say no.

In addition, it is more challenging to be positive than negative—much harder, according to some studies.[2] Staying positive takes work, a deliberate plan, and a sustained effort. Since it requires deliberate intent to migrate from negative emotions to positive ones, this transition often requires a stress-recovery mechanism. Balancing stress expenditure with stress recovery must be practiced on a daily basis if we are to succeed in performing well under pressure.

The Breath of Life

There are many ways to recover and move from negative to positive emotional quadrants, but the quickest way of all is through breathing. I realize that this may sound overly simplistic, so I will explain. Oxygen is necessary for our survival. We can live days without food or water, but not even minutes without oxygen. Our body cannot function without it. In sports science, fitness is defined by the speed at which oxygen is transferred from the lungs to the heart and muscles and to the blood cells of our body.[3] A person with a high level of fitness can transfer high amounts of oxygen to the body, just like a person with low levels of fitness will transfer low levels of oxygen. Can you now see how breathing (the intake of oxygen) is directly tied to our physiology?

As I explained, the word *emote* comes from the Latin word meaning "to put in motion." Therefore, as breath (oxygen) puts the body in motion, our emotions also put the body in motion.

Think about it. When you become scared and need to run from something like a burning fire, your respiratory rate increases. Why? Because your body needs the oxygen in order to flee the scene so you can return to safety. It was the emotion that caused your breathing pattern to shift. Doesn't it make sense, then, that we can control our emotions and therefore our physiology with particular breathing patterns? It just doesn't seem possible that we could stay angry while taking long, slow breaths in and out, does it? Pause now and take some long deep breaths in and out through your nose. Do you feel the difference?

Listed are the breath prints for the quadrants. Practice these breathing patterns, and you will feel the connection:

Breathing for Your Emotions

HIGH NEGATIVE	HIGH POSITIVE
Shallow breath in through the mouth and a *fast breath out* through the mouth . . . the beginning of hyperventilation. This is the fight-or-flight breath.	*Fast, deep breath in* through the nose and a *fast breath out* through the mouth.
LOW NEGATIVE	**LOW POSITIVE**
Shallow breath in and a *slow breath out* through the mouth . . . the breath of a sigh.	*Deep, slow breath in* through the nose and a *slow breath out* through the nose. It is a relaxing, calming breath. For the most relaxing breath, make your exhale twice as long as the inhale. This is the breath most often used in yoga.

Whatever quadrant we are in emotionally, we breathe according to the breath print of that quadrant; it is natural, and it is physiological. The fastest way to change emotional quadrants is by breathing according to the breath print of the quadrant where we want to go. For example, if we are in the high-negative quadrant—angry or fearful—and want to move to the positive side, the quickest way is to take three high-positive breaths: deep in through the nose and fast out through the mouth.

Breathing in this way transports enough oxygen into our bloodstream so that our system interprets that we are moving in that direction physiologically. Our emotions must follow, because emotions and breath are interconnected. Practice this consciously every day, and you will gain not only critical awareness about your body but also control over your emotions and stressful situations. Regulating your emotions is critical to health and peak performance. How does it feel to know that it's this easy to elevate yourself to a "thriving" status—as practiced by the elite athletes and top military personnel that I coach? As I said before, it just takes training and practice.

Setting Yourself Up to Win

Now you know one of the quickest ways to work with your emotions and navigate stress—through breathing. Here are some additional tips for moving from negative to positive states. Use the suggestions here while adding ones of your own to strengthen those areas of weakness. Practice these tips with the breathing patterns for maximum benefits.

MENTAL

- Focus on what is in your control and look for the positive in every situation.
- At the end of the day, take a quick mental inventory of the day's victories. They all count, no matter how small or large.
- Certain conditions are truly temporary; see them as such.

EMOTIONAL

- When you recognize that you aren't handling stress well, talk to someone about how you are feeling.
- There is *always* something to appreciate and be grateful for. In emotionally charged situations, gratitude and appreciation interrupt the negative emotional cycle and put you instantly in a more positive state.

SPIRITUAL

- Focus on your intentions and purpose in the situation—it will give you inspiration.

- Remember the big picture while handling the little details of the day.
- Let go of asking "Why?" and instead ask, "What is the best thing I can do right now?"

PHYSICAL

- Take regular breaks every ninety minutes, even if it's just for a few minutes.
- Drink water regularly; it's critical to stay well hydrated and balanced.
- Eat small but frequent meals or healthy, low-fat, low-sugar snacks, with little food prior to bedtime.
- Do your best to go to bed at the same time each night. Prior to falling asleep, focus on positive thoughts and expect a restful and restorative sleep experience.

PERFORMANCE-BOOSTING STRATEGIES

1. Evaluate your emotional acuity. Think of a situation where you reacted negatively and lost control of your emotions. Envision that situation and ask yourself: "What was I thinking, and how did that affect my emotions? What outcome could have been achieved had I taken control of my emotions through breathing?"
2. What positive benefits do you see in having a practiced and calm response?
3. Next time you find yourself in a stressful or frustrating situation, practice using your breath to take control of your negative emotions and transition them as quickly as possible to positive ones. Trust me, you will reap the rewards!

CHAPTER 6

Preparing for Performance under Pressure

"Skill is only developed by hours and hours of work."
Usain Bolt, gold medal–winning Olympic sprinter

My good friend John Li, MD, is one of a few specialists in the country who can perform ear surgery with the Esteem totally implantable device (similar to a cochlear implant but more complex). The procedure is so technically difficult and the margin of error so narrow that the makers of the device actually auditioned and tested two hundred ear surgeons to select about ten worldwide in order to maintain quality control. The device is an amazing technological breakthrough that allows patients to hear without visible hearing aids. Patients are able to live in freedom, swim, exercise, and work without anything plugging the ear canals. John's patients often use the word *miraculous* as they take in the magnificent sounds of the world around them.

I had the opportunity to join John for his morning preparation regimen before a day of surgery. What I witnessed was an incredibly meticulous process to prepare for a highly demanding day in the operating room. John knows that his detailed and precise morning routine is essential for a successful surgery. The process involves the whole team and includes administering careful anesthesia, applying facial nerve electrodes to monitor the facial nerve, sterilizing the tools and prepping the patient, checking the tools and procedures to perform, communicating with the surgery team in the operating room, and finally praying for a swift and accurate procedure.

Without such careful preparation, a procedure such as this could have unfortunate—or even tragic—results. John's dedication to preparedness can serve as an example for all of us. That's because daily stress preparation truly makes the difference between success and failure in any venture.

Be Prepared!

The Scouts' motto "Be prepared" is an excellent motto for all of us and all of life. It is also essential for anyone interested in life mastery. Many people simply go through life like they're driving bumper cars, never knowing when or where they are going to get hit. They spend all their time just trying to make it around the track successfully. When the really big collisions of life arrive, they are caught totally unaware and unprepared, often with disastrous results.

None of us can predict all the storms of life that will come our way. But we can prepare ourselves for life so that gravity, however big or small, will elicit from us a consistent response of excellence and elite performance. We can weather the storms successfully without losing our cool or squandering our energy reserves.

Show me a person's level of commitment to preparation, and I will show you that person's capacity to succeed in whatever he or she sets out to do in the midst of stress. Prepared people are rarely surprised, because they live in expectancy of what is to come instead of avoiding a future filled with potential challenges.

Some people ask whether it is really possible to prepare for gravity or crises. "Crises are unpredictable," they say. Yes, but crises are also inevitable. If we know this reality, we can prepare for any storm by developing a better relationship with stress *now*. Even if we do not know the specific form our storm might take, we will be better prepared.

The essence of performing well under pressure is integrating stress through preparation and practice so that our entire relationship with stress and gravity is permanently shifted. In one sense, when we practice this, everything becomes much less of a big deal, and we are able to take more things in stride.

Emergency room personnel work in a high-stress environment where they deal with crisis situations all the time. While they never know in advance what emergencies they will face, their education and training have prepared them to deal with what comes through the doors, whether it's a heart attack, a gunshot wound, an epileptic seizure, or a diabetic coma. Their secret is preparation, which implies knowledge, training, and practice.

Handling stress effectively involves two critical umbrella components: the ability to see stress positively (as a challenge critical to success) rather than negatively (as a threat), and the ability to create regular mental, emotional, spiritual, and physical alignment, or what I call "MESP alignment." Alignment in this context means achieving harmony or congruence in the four areas that make up each individual. It means you feel in sync with yourself. (In chapter 9, we will discuss MESP alignment in more detail.)

All the tools, tips, suggestions, information, and coaching that I share in this book are directed toward these two goals of viewing stress positively and achieving MESP alignment. If you do not reach these goals, you will find that stress will likely continue to control you, rather than the other way around. Further, it will be all but impossible to operate at your thrive level, since thriving requires the mastery of stress.

Success does not occur in a vacuum, and it doesn't happen accidentally or immediately. For example, military fighter pilots spend thousands of hours preparing to fly missions in war-torn areas to protect our country. Without the commitment and the discipline of real-world simulation training, these elite individuals would not be able to perform their missions safely with precision and excellence in times of real crisis. This is the key to staying calm under pressure when every detail matters.

I have watched pilots go through systems checks every single time they fly, the same way with the same information and the same criteria. To the untrained eye, it looks like a lot of redundancy, but to the trained eye it is the essence of professionalism and prepared excellence.

Why do pilots take so much time preparing before each flight? Because they operate in an environment with zero tolerance for errors: if anyone makes a mistake, someone may die. That is why, to guarantee success, it is absolutely necessary for every detail to be checked.

I have the privilege of training fighter pilots for the United States Air Force in stress preparation and in post-deployment stress debriefing. I have seen firsthand the time, effort, and energy that goes into their military training to ensure a high level of performance. Over the years, I have assisted in enhancing their performance by teaching them about the body's natural biorhythms in dealing with stress, as well as the critical nature of life balance in stress preparation.

You may be thinking, "That's great but I'm not a fighter pilot." The good news is that everyone—from business leaders to world-class athletes to teenagers to new parents—will benefit from the power of training and preparation. New parents can shift their schedules in advance to allow for more rest. Teens can prepare for peer pressure by working with a trained professional, a parent, or a trusted adult to build a healthy self-image and understand the nature of competition from peers. Business leaders can prep for important presentations by practicing over and over until talking about their material becomes natural.

Not only are your training and preparation vital, but so is your outlook. Be ready for something great to happen personally, relationally, or occupationally—and believe that it *can*. I've seen many people who are desperate for something great to happen in their lives but at the same time are convinced that it cannot possibly happen for them. As I tell my clients, choose to see everything, including stress, more positively, and prepare for good things to happen. Once you see how positive thinking creates results, you will experience tremendous momentum, ultimately finding it easier to deal with the stresses that do arise.

Living Your Life's Purpose

Your life's purpose is essentially your reason for living and an overriding inspiration for all your actions. Everyone has a life purpose, whether they know it or not. Often it can be seen in their choice of career. For example, people who strive to educate often become counselors, coaches, writers, ministers, professors, or schoolteachers. Those who desire to preserve safety and security may become policy officers, firefighters, diplomats, or members of the military. Those who want to create might become business owners, artisans, musicians, or marketing executives. People who like to lead others may become corporate executives, managers, or government officials, while people who prefer to support often find themselves in finance, administration, or transportation roles. Still others who aim to care for others' health might become doctors, nurses, nutritionists, or fitness instructors.

There are many life purposes, and sometimes we have more than one. However, generally only one or two will really call to you. Some people understand their life's purpose from an early age, and others identify it through education, training, and experience. Living your life's purpose successfully simply means recognizing its significance in every area of your life and making choices to support it daily. (If you are unsure what your life's purpose is, there are many great resources to help you find it. One of my favorites is *The Purpose Driven Life* by Rick Warren.)

Under the umbrella of life purpose is your life's work, which is the profession, job, or occupation that helps you live your larger purpose. Successful people find the best ways to accomplish their life's purpose. They know what they want to do and are determined to do it, and they prepare themselves mentally, emotionally, spiritually, and physically so that nothing will prevent them from carrying it out.

Purpose isn't always linked to a career, though. It could be linked to your role as a loving parent, or as an advocate for justice, or as someone dedicated to helping the less fortunate. Most important, purpose is not something you arrive at; it is something that you live and experience every day.

The first and most critical aspect of setting yourself up for success in the area of work (whether it is paid or volunteer) is to do something you love. Automatically, you significantly reduce stress levels by choosing work that is enjoyable. Once you find and choose work that you love, being successful at that work requires a three-phase process: *preparation*, *performance*, and *post-preparation* (or debriefing).

Get Ready

Let's take a more detailed look at the first phase—preparation. The degree of preparation required for one's life work is generally related to the degree to which an error would compromise lives or, on the other end of the scale, enjoyment. People who work in zero-error-tolerance environments such as aerospace, medicine, the military, and engineering usually follow the philosophy of "Expect the best, but plan for the worst." This key operative also applies to professions with a purpose of maintaining safety and health. In these situations, errors cost lives, so preparation must include an exhaustive look at worst-case scenarios and an analysis of how to maximize safety, quality, and productivity.

This zero-error-tolerance environment is also at play for a few people in very high-paying or high-profile positions and in industries that are extremely competitive and demand high performance, such as sports and the upper echelons of politics and business. These people, because of their income and position, are expected to perform at the highest levels and make fewer errors or risk losing their job.

Other work allows for more error, but higher levels of preparation will secure a better chance of enjoyment and better performance under pressure. Anticipating potential problems and having a contingency plan for dealing with them is smart. But as with everything in life, there is a point of diminishing returns—where the effort and energy you are expending to prepare will outweigh the potential gain of the preparation. (This is often the case with people who suffer from chronic anxiety and become overly stressed about every detail. In these situations, it may be better to relax during the preparation phase rather than overplan.)

How you manage your life's mission in terms of preparation is up to you. I manage mine to zero tolerance—preparing for the worst but expecting the best—because I am committed to the highest possible performance for my sake and for those around me. When I awaken each day, I contemplate the things that are right in my life versus focusing on what may be going less than perfectly. This is the first key to making every day a great day. Even though there may be some difficult moments or hours, the key is to have the necessary training and recovery speed to shift any unhealthy, consuming focuses to positive ones for an overall net-positive day.

My mission allows for more error than a firefighter, but I still play it like a firefighter. I aim to have an attitude that is ready for anything, anticipating potential crises from a calm mind/body state. This is a model of excellence that many have used to become the best they can be in their fields.

I mentioned this earlier, but it is such a key principle in fulfilling our life's purpose that it bears repeating: *no one will ever consistently outperform his or her training.* This means that we must train the way we expect to perform. Do you want to be the best you can be? Then train to be the best! If it you want to be the best skier, you need to train like the best skier. Find a coach; train with people who challenge you; practice strength training multiple times a week; get on the mountain every single day. If you want to be the best teacher, train to be the best teacher. Take additional classes; learn new ways to manage your classroom; compare notes with colleagues you admire; design a foolproof system for lesson planning. Don't train for where you are now. Train and prepare for where you want to go, fully believing and seeing your desired reality.

Many people fail under pressure simply because they did not prepare correctly. Preparation can give you the confidence to perform well in a high-pressure situation. The best way to fight off nerves in public speaking, for example, is to be highly prepared, knowing the information and the audience thoroughly and then trusting the training instincts to kick in when it's time to deliver.

People often ask me how to find luck. They say, "You've been lucky in your life because of all the things you've been able to accomplish." My common response is simple: "It is not luck. It is preparation meeting opportunity." I look at luck as simply an opportunity I have not yet met. That is why I place such importance on training and preparation. Unless we train and prepare, we will miss opportunity when it comes our way. Training and preparation are actions that anticipate greatness. When we train and prepare, we are saying we are willing to claim the opportunities that come our way as gifts that validate our desired realities.

Applying this principle of *preparation meeting opportunity* is what separates those who perform well under pressure from those who do not. If you are not prepared, you will falter under challenging or demanding circumstances—and this will only increase your stress.

Life's Work in Action

The second phase in becoming successful in your life's work is the performance itself. This simply means that our performance will reveal how well we have trained. The adequacy or inadequacy of our training will come out under pressure.

Have you ever seen people who were so cool under pressure that you thought they had ice in their veins? These people have learned to be prepared. Learning from our mistakes is one of the first keys to learning how to duplicate our successes. Quite often, these superperformers have learned their lessons about preparedness through the hard knocks of failure due to lack of preparedness.

Elite performers have learned how to turn the stress of performance into an opportunity to excel, regardless of who is watching or what is at stake. It may be the bottom of the ninth inning in the championship game with two outs, two strikes, and the winning run on third. Pressure? Just a little! But elite performers treat that next pitch just like any other. Their concentration, calmness, and focus come from having thrown thousands of pitches in preseason training, successful executions in other jams, and a delivery ritual practiced for years. When that stress comes, they are ready.

Some players have reported that their intense focus silenced an otherwise deafening crowd just prior to a key play. This is called being "in the zone." What's more, elite performers live for moments like this, moments that test them, because they believe they have been put on the planet for just such moments. Their purpose, whatever their field, is to be dependable in a pinch and to consistently perform with excellence—both under pressure and on demand. Medical personnel who choose the emergency room versus private practice are another perfect example of people who love the challenge of rising to every occasion; they enjoy the pressure of putting their skills to the test in stressful and life-altering situations.

I have trained in such a way that I love the pressure of not knowing what's going to happen. That is why I still enjoy live radio and television as a "performance" that offers me the opportunity to trust my pre-camera preparation. I have the challenge and opportunity to speak as a calm responder under pressure. This also has prepared me—although with strikingly different stakes and stress levels—for helping people during life-altering crises, such as natural disasters and other mass tragedies. During high-stress events, I am able to access information and processes with mental clarity and emotional confidence due to my training.

This love of the challenge that all elite performers share is partly genetic, but it is also a learned behavior. Not everybody is wired for high-pressure/high-stakes positions, but anyone who wants to be can be trained for it.

Stress preparation adds a skill set that will help you to maximize success. And it works whether you are a star athlete, a midlevel manager pushing for a promotion, or a new parent training for your first triathlon.

This inspiration to be the best comes from understanding that we can always expand our capacity for excellence no matter what the situation, as long as we recognize the stress opportunity as a challenge instead of a threat. Nothing quite equals the satisfaction of knowing that we have excelled or even exceeded our own expectations.

Debrief, Debrief, Debrief

All three phases of the process are equally important in relation to stress. Ignoring any one of them significantly increases one's probability of delivering a mediocre performance or even failing.

The final phase is post-preparation or post-performance debriefing. Debriefing should be done after every important event to maximize performance. For instance, company leaders should debrief after company conferences, evaluating things such as the outcome of the discussions, the effectiveness of keynote speakers, and whether the right people attended the right meetings. If the conference had technical difficulties or the meetings ran too long, those problems should be noted, with the responsible parties in attendance to discuss solutions. Even when things have gone well, it's helpful to debrief in order to duplicate the results again.

Many people skip the debriefing process either because they want to move forward or because they don't want to revisit a challenging or painful situation. In the case where emotions are heightened, however, debriefing is absolutely crucial. For example, I am a United States Defense Department contractor who regularly debriefs soldiers returning from war, helping them process mental and emotional pain to re-enter and adjust to life back home. I assist these individuals in reconnecting with their families and former lives through a debriefing process of three steps: venting, releasing (or letting go), and realigning (with their healthy and positive vision for themselves and their lives).

The time it takes to debrief depends both on the individual and the situation. However, returning to a somewhat normal lifestyle with the help of a trained professional relieves much of the post-traumatic stress of having been in a war zone. I worked with one young man who was struggling with nightmares and flashbacks. We began with writing stories of what happened and then burning them to release the internal toxic waste so healing could begin. After several sessions of writing and discussing these events, I helped him visualize his future—in living color and with excitement—to counterbalance painful memories. Articulating a compelling future can radically alter the perception and reality of pain, helping inspire a new beginning of hope and wonder.

The debriefing phase is just as important as the preparation and performance phases. It sets the stage for the future, ensuring that the right steps are taken to achieve success. Without proper and healthy debriefing, the next event, conflict, job, or relationship may be compromised by pent-up energy and unprocessed emotion that can skew a person's perception of reality.

People with a distorted sense of reality cannot experience or live life to the fullest. The best they can hope for is to merely survive life from day to day. This is why it is so important to evaluate the performance stage and embrace the emotions surrounding it. This debriefing enables us to move beyond mere survival mode into the fullness of life.

Debriefing from Trauma

Debriefing after an important event, such as a conference or an emotionally charged meeting, is one thing. But what about debriefing after a highly traumatic event? As a coach and psychologist, I've spent countless hours helping clients and elite athletes overcome their stress and perform at peak levels. But my own ability to help others perform under pressure was first tested in 2001, when I was called upon to assist after the terrorist attacks of 9/11.

Walking into Ground Zero in New York City for the first time was an assault on my senses. It was coupled with the sorrow that accompanies the realization that our homeland had suffered an enormous blow. Focusing through the smoke and ash, I saw in the distance a thirty-foot iron beam in the shape of a cross. Off to the side was a huge American flag attached to the side of a torn and burned building. It was like a scene from a war movie.

For the next three months, I conducted crisis trainings in blown-out office buildings. During this time, I heard hundreds of stories of shock, panic, and disbelief—stories I had never heard before. After all, this was a new type of disaster for me—one created by humans, not nature.

I can still remember the details of the wreckage and can still smell that site as it burned over the course of those three months. I also remember the innumerable courageous men and women assisting those consumed by shock and grief. Part of our role in helping these people work through stress was to grieve with them, but to also help them realize that life would never be the same for them or any of us. Through this process of discovery and recovery, they could eventually regain hope and meet life from a different but inspired place.

As I learned during my time at Ground Zero, the first key to debriefing from trauma is learning how to filter, categorize, and interpret one's emotions, thought processes, and mental images. If you are suffering from trauma, remember that your emotions can be controlled for periods of time by breathing correctly, moving and exercising on a regular basis, and talking with someone who can relate to your specific needs. Depending on the level of trauma and the severity of the situation, however, you must process your emotions and memories in order to recover properly and walk through life with more balance.

This is a critical part of the debriefing process, particularly after a painful event. Unless you learn how to vent safely and in healthy ways through a therapeutic process, negative emotions will build up inside until finally they spill over as a form of toxic waste.

The second key to successfully debriefing from trauma is to acknowledge that you have had an experience that must be processed. Accepting the truth of any trauma is a major step toward regaining your health, happiness, and productivity. If you skip this phase, you can easily end up in denial. Denial will work for only a short time, because reality will confront you constantly and eventually require you to move on. When you forgive, you can heal from your past failures and move into a healthy space.

Recognizing that failure, trauma, or crisis can be a positive turning point is a major step forward in a successful debriefing process. This stage of the process can take a while to get through, depending on the ability of the individual to let go of any internalized or repressed feelings. Letting go is not easy, but you must learn always to be honest with yourself. The good news is that you can heal and grow if you acknowledge where you have been and look ahead with hope and deeper understanding.

The third key to successfully debriefing from trauma is committing to the process itself. This is the ability to continue with the venting phase for as long as it takes to come to increasing levels of peace with it. Trauma can heal over time, and the process happens in stages. With the guidance of a professional, you can learn what needs healing while acknowledging any new layers of the issue. This final process can go on for a lifetime. Do not be discouraged by this; there are many highly successful people who process trauma for all of their lives. Having past trauma does not mean that you cannot thrive. You can. In fact, the healing of your trauma may be integral to your life's work and ability to thrive under pressure.

PERFORMANCE-BOOSTING STRATEGIES

1. Focus on one issue in your life that you would like to address. Then write out several points in response to these questions: What do I want? What do I need to do to get it (preparation)? What actions do I need to take, and what challenges can I anticipate? How do I see myself resolving these challenges?
2. Remember that you will never consistently outperform your training. So train today like it is your last day on earth and you have one final opportunity to perform. Make it count!

CHAPTER 7

Managing the Body and Physical Stress

"To keep the body in good health is a duty,
otherwise we shall not be able to keep our mind strong and clear."
Buddha

I coached a government official who was a hard-driving leader with little awareness of the price that comes from working at relentless levels of intensity without sufficient recovery. After training his entire staff on how to navigate daily stress and maximize performance, I received a call that this official had suffered a massive heart attack. He had been just moments from death before EMTs arrived to save his life and rush him to the hospital.

After triple-bypass heart surgery and weeks of recovery, he returned to work much more relaxed, stating that life is a gift and work is an extension of that lifestyle.

Life without physical health and well-being is a breakdown waiting to happen. Thankfully, we can avoid a physical, emotional, or mental collapse by learning the difficult lesson of managing physical stress and applying that lesson to empower all other aspects of life. If we want to perform well under pressure, we must keep both our mind and body functioning at optimal levels.

Stress Manifestations

Unprocessed stress of any kind eventually manifests in physical symptoms. These symptoms generally present in one or more of three primary areas: immunity, inflammation, and infection.

Prolonged stress without relief and recovery releases toxins into the cells of our body. When the toxicity of our body reaches a certain level of concentration, our immune system may become compromised. Chronic stress may also result in inflammation that targets previously weakened bodily organs or systems.[1]

Prolonged inflammation can lead to significant, chronic health problems and a host of diseases. Simply treating the condition with antibiotics or other medication is not enough. The symptoms might go away for a while, but unless we first address the harmful stress that caused the inflammation, our health will suffer. In fact, eliminating harmful toxic buildup in the body brought on by negative stress is key to avoiding a compromised immune system, thus preventing everything from inflammation to infection to the common cold.[2]

To deal with these issues of weakened immunity, inflammation, and infection, we have historically turned to medication. Unfortunately, our society has become overmedicated; we think we can fix every health problem with a pill or surgery.[3] Don't misunderstand—I believe medical science as a whole has been a great boon to humanity, but a better solution is to *prevent* health problems by ensuring that we get adequate nutrition, exercise, hydration, and rest. Plus, we should participate in recovery cycles and other practices to master our stress on a daily basis.

Eating for Energy and Nutrient Balance

Prevention starts with nutrition. Sadly, in spite of all the advances in modern medicine and our knowledge of health, Americans today are more overweight and less healthy than at any other time in our history.[4] Just 23 percent of Americans get enough exercise on a daily basis.[5] With our penchant for eating sugary, starchy, and high-fat foods, it is no surprise that more than 71 percent of us are overweight[6] and that the levels of diabetes and heart disease have risen dramatically among both adults and children.[7]

How can this be? Because we don't know what or how to eat!

It seems that every week a new study exposes the dangers of eating a certain kind of food. The very next week, another study comes out contradicting the first one. Add to this all the experts touting new miracle diets or pills, and the result is general confusion regarding healthy eating.

Even when we know how to eat properly, many of us don't do it because we feel like we don't have the time or the money. Life is too fast. But eating on the run is a guaranteed stress builder and a certain formula for nutritional and physical health disasters.

As I travel the nation, speaking at conferences and working with clients, my observation is that Americans sorely underestimate the importance of food, nutrition, and exercise as it relates to performance and stress. We have collectively created heavy gravity for ourselves and are in great need of change. We cannot thrive in life or handle stress successfully without giving our body all that it needs, though. It's the only one we've got!

Much of what I've learned about nutrition and physical fitness has come from my wife, Marsha Pitt Lyles. The guidance in this chapter (and in this book's detailed appendix) comes from her decades of experience as a fitness trainer and dancer.

As I mentioned in chapter 4, society has programmed us to adopt eating habits that impede optimal health, encouraging us to consume two or three heavy meals a day. In contrast, I coach my elite athletes to give their bodies a consistent supply of fuel—small amounts of healthy food—every three hours. For them, it is like throwing logs on a fire at regular intervals to keep it burning.

There is much debate about how often to eat, even among nutritionists, but in my two decades of coaching, I have seen hundreds of clients reduce stress and maximize their performance by eating five or six small, healthy meals each day. When we eat every three hours, we will find it easier to concentrate on the task at hand.[8] And when we are able to concentrate by supplying our body with nourishing food, we can function at a high level.

Common sense tells us that if we increase the frequency of our eating, we should then decrease the size of our meals. Eating smaller portions is good advice no matter how often we eat. Most people who eat only two or three meals a day eat more than they should at each meal. But consuming more food than we can process during each cycle simply drains our energy and adds to our waistline. Our body requires concentrated energy to digest food. Why do you think we feel sleepy after a big meal?

Peak performers in every field know better than to eat a heavy meal before a game, presentation, or meeting. If they do, their efficiency and performance suffer. It's the same way for all of us: heavy meals limit our performance, no matter what we are doing.

I coach my clients to eat three small meals a day interspersed with three light snacks. By "small," I mean 500- to 800-calorie meals (depending on how many calories are needed to sustain your ideal body weight) that balance complex carbohydrates and proteins. A light snack would be around 200 to 250 calories. (This is for an average person; athletes typically require more.)

One key to good nutrition is eating a healthy, ample breakfast. Many people skip breakfast because they think they don't have the time or they don't like to eat early in the day. They are cheating themselves out of high energy levels and the opportunity for peak performance. Conclusive studies have shown that children who eat breakfast every day consistently perform better in school than those who do not eat breakfast.[9] Studies also show that peak levels of brain function occur in late morning hours, so skipping breakfast actually hurts our performance.[10]

Another way to improve our general nutrition is to reduce our consumption of unhealthy fats and simple sugars. During the 1990s, health-conscious Americans went on a no-fat or low-fat diet frenzy in an effort to lose weight. The irony is that the per capita obesity rate for Americans actually increased by 15 to 20 percent during that time.[11] What happened? Food companies provided low-fat and no-fat food to meet the public demand, but to restore the taste lost by removing the fat, they doubled or even tripled the sugar content. Since our bodies store any unused carbohydrates (sugars) as fat, it is no surprise that so many Americans got fatter eating fat-free foods. Our bodies need healthy fats, such as those found in avocados, nuts, and seeds. So eliminating all fats is *not* the way to go.

Interestingly, since then the pendulum has swung the other way. Today, many people are embracing the opposite of the 1990s low-fat plan—the high-protein, low-carb diet. As I tell my clients, these diets may be popular, but they are unhealthy and ineffective for long-term weight stabilization. They can also lead to rapid energy loss. The excess protein and fat consumed in these diets can only be burned off with high amounts of exercise. Moreover, these diets often lead to other types of health and nutritional problems.[12]

The bottom line: the foods we eat greatly affect our mood, energy, and performance. If we eat a whole-food, predominantly plant-based diet, we are likely to get all the nutritional support we need.[13] In addition, if we eat a variety of healthy foods, we will have more energy to exercise, our mood will be better, and we will be less prone to cheat on our new healthy eating habits, because we won't feel deprived.

As we know now, when we focus on all elements of our body—mental, emotional, spiritual, and physical—we are on the high road to success. So how can we create a positive change in our body to maximize performance? Start with these strategies:

Step 1: Assessment

First, find out what is currently happening in your body. Besides knowing the basics, such as your body mass index (BMI) and approximately how many calories you need each day, you must measure your work/rest cycles, meaning how much and how hard you work/workout and how well you sufficiently recover.

Part of this recovery includes how many hours you sleep and how well you recover during sleep. As discussed previously, sleep and rest are two entirely different matters; sleep is physical recovery, while rest is spiritual recovery. How many times have you slept all night and woken up tired? Or how many times have you taken a catnap and felt like you slept all night? That's the difference between sleep and rest recovery.

In addition, you must identify all the factors that have prevented you from staying with a previous plan to get physically healthy—whether it has been work or relationship stress, addiction, bad habits, and so forth. Recognizing these factors is essential for creating a plan that will work.

Step 2: Diagnosis

Next, identify the specific challenges that you are facing and where your stress may originate. Once you've gathered all the information in step 1, you may want to meet with a nutritionist to get a sense of the realities of your current eating plan.

If you need to, keep a sleep and rest log for a week with notes about your energy levels and the foods you ate. It is easy to determine where diet-related stress may be occurring when you keep a record of results. For instance, if you eat a heavy meal late in the day, your sleep will be affected later that night and you will wake up the next morning feeling sluggish. Be sure to note information like this, so that when you sit down at the end of the week, you will be prepared to develop a specific action plan. Until you know how physically stressed you are—for example, whether you "crash" when you sleep rather than actually recover—you won't know what to change.

Lastly, if you have any mental and emotional challenges linked to food (such as an eating disorder), seek support from a therapist or coach.

Step 3: Prescription

After you've completed steps 1 and 2, you are ready to create and implement a plan of action. This "prescription" will address a portion or all of the points you noted in step 2, bringing you closer to achieving your goal of thriving under pressure.

To help you implement healthy changes, I've included some general information about nutrition as well as a simple strategy to keep you on track whether you're cooking at home or eating on the road. (If you'd like more detailed nutrition information, reference the appendix in the back of this book.)

The Eyeball Method

We get energy from fats, proteins, and carbohydrates—but we obtain energy most quickly by eating simple or complex carbohydrates (the latter is preferred). Over the years, I've found a simple, commonsense way to balance the proteins and complex carbohydrates that we need in the correct proportions. It does not involve measuring portions or counting calories. Better yet, there are no foods that are totally off limits. Again, moderation is the key, along with intention: eating with an eye to fueling our body only with what it will need until the next pit stop. This method is so effective that I use it myself and prescribe it for my performance clients. It's like dieting with the eyes—using the "eyeball method."

Success with the eyeball method involves three basic things:

- Understanding the difference between proteins, simple carbohydrates, and complex carbohydrates. This will help you know what foods to choose.
- Understanding how each food will affect your system—whether it will act as an accelerator or as a brake during the three-hour cycle. This knowledge is critical for determining what to eat at certain times of the day.
- Understanding how each food will affect your performance.

With this knowledge, we can make informed decisions regarding what we eat and when. In principle, the eyeball method is simple. The biggest challenge is learning to think differently about food. Most of us select our food primarily based on taste. With the eyeball method, we choose foods and combinations of foods based on how they function in our body (either as an accelerator or a brake). This method makes us think ahead to what is needed in the next few hours while keeping in mind the necessary balance between proteins and carbohydrates.

Here's how it works. Imagine that you are standing in a buffet line. First, you locate the proteins and the carbohydrates. Next, you mentally separate the simple carbohydrates from the complex carbohydrates. Finally, you make your food selections to ensure the proper ratio between proteins and carbohydrates, and to reflect an understanding of the amount of energy you plan on expending in the next few hours.

Following the eyeball method, you may choose a chicken breast or some lean roast beef for your protein source. For balance on the carbohydrate side, you might select a couple of vegetables, such as green beans and carrots. If you want some bread, check first to see whether it is white, whole grain, or multigrain bread. If it is white bread, you may choose to pass on it, particularly if you plan to eat dessert. If your vegetables and "dark" bread make your plate a little heavy on the carbohydrate side, you may choose an additional protein source, such as a little bit of cheese, to bring everything into balance.

Finding the right mix for you may take some time and experimentation. Tune in to your body; it will tell you when something works for you and when it does not. If you find that you can barely keep your eyes open after a meal, then take notice and make adjustments.

Once you become comfortable with this approach, it will quickly become second nature. Enjoy all the foods you like, but focus on moderation and balance. And remember to keep the portions small: you will be eating again in three hours.

Exercise Matters . . . and It Works

We all know the importance of exercise. Exercise goes hand in hand with proper nutrition in controlling obesity, improving overall health, and enabling us to convert bad stress into good stress. Diet alone is not enough.

It is the combination of diet and regular physical activity that makes the real difference for our long-term good health and our ability to process stress successfully. Even one brisk thirty-minute walk every day will make a significant difference in improving our health and energy levels.[14]

Think of exercise as meditation in motion. Exercise will improve your mood because it allows the brain to release endorphins—chemicals released by your pituitary gland that make you feel happy and block out pain. According to the Mayo Clinic, regular exercise can increase self-confidence and lower the symptoms associated with mild depression and anxiety.[15] Exercise also can improve your sleep. All this can ease your stress levels and give you a sense of command over your body and your life.

You need aerobic exercise to burn fat and condition your heart and lungs, and resistance training to build lean muscle. Aerobic exercise doesn't have to involve hours and hours in the gym or pounding pavement, though. Four 25- to 40-minute sessions a week are sufficient.[16] That is less than three hours a week, which can help add years to your life span and enhance the quality of your life.

Resistance training should be done preferably three to four times a week, thirty to forty minutes a session.[17] This doesn't have to be pumping heavy weights in a gym. You can do exercises such as push-ups, curls, or abdominal crunches to support the back, and light weightlifting with small barbells or on Nautilus machines. Your personal program can be as simple or as elaborate as your inclination and budget dictate. Even an inexpensive, elastic exercise band can produce excellent results.

Another important aspect is regular stretching to develop flexibility. A mild warm-up with stretching helps prepare your muscles and tendons more gradually for higher-intensity demands, reducing the risk of injury during workouts.

In addition to deliberate exercise, you can incorporate healthy physical activity into your daily routine. For example, when shopping or running errands, avoid parking close to the entrance. Whenever possible, take the stairs instead of the elevator or escalator. At work, stand up every couple of hours and take a stretch break or go for a short walk—anything to inject extra movement into the day's routine. Some activity is better than none, and often the best way to make a change is to begin with small steps.

Whatever workout regimen you choose, get input from a trained professional on proper form; poor form leads to injuries and is counterproductive. And be consistent. Consistency is the key to success. You'll be amazed at how quickly you will feel better physically and mentally—and how much better equipped you will be for quickly converting harmful stress into good stress so you can live the life you desire.

PERFORMANCE-BOOSTING STRATEGIES

1. Commit to making one permanent shift in the area of physical fitness and nutrition. Determine what it is you want to do and the actions required.
2. Prepare for this change by anticipating challenges and putting a system in place for success. Remember that something becomes a habit in a very short time when we are inspired and prepared. Just fall forward into the success that you envision, creating and maintaining higher and higher levels of physical energy.

CHAPTER 8

Taming Technostress

"Everybody gets so much information all day long that they lose their common sense."
Gertrude Stein, author

Stress has been a part of life from the very beginning of time, but technology has now created a new stressor that most of us are still trying to navigate. Technostress is a modern-day condition of maladaptation caused by our inability to cope with computing technologies in a healthy manner. (Meaning, we love our technology but most of us don't know how to manage it well!)

One example is the way smartphones have changed our lives, giving us instant and continuous access to communicate and work from anywhere. I remember talking on a phone that hung from our kitchen wall in our home when I was young. The cord was so short that I had to sit on the floor underneath the phone. Now smartphones and Wi-Fi have connected us with one another in a mobile/global community all the time, whether we are sitting on an airplane to Europe or on a park bench in our local neighborhood.

Technology generally causes a numbing of the senses—glazed-over eyes, frequent headaches, chronic backache, poor attention span, and a loss of interest in engaging with nature or being active. Don't get me wrong, I love my technology and use it daily just like everyone else. But I also hear many stories of how individuals are tethered to technology. Sadly, they are more focused on their machines than on people.

Do you sleep with your mobile device? Do you use it as your alarm clock? Do you store your music, get your mobile entertainment, buy household staples, and text people on your phone? What else literally goes to bed with or near you, wakes up with you, is the first thing you grab in the morning, and then stays attached to you all day? For most of us, there have been few things that have garnered so much of our attention in life—other than maybe a loving pet, a favorite car, or our feelings associated with a new romantic interest.

Granted, some of us might take our car to bed if we could (don't laugh). But in truth, most people have no place to retreat and hide—even for a few minutes—without wondering what is happening in the digital world. This constant connection says a lot about what is happening to us as a culture as technological advances are outpacing most of us on a daily basis. Some people seem to enjoy keeping up, but many others feel behind on the latest trends. I've witnessed this with clients who are part of my generation, the last pre-computer generation, which also means the last pre-Facebook/Twitter/Instagram generation.

While I sit here and fumble around with my smartphone—which outsmarts me most of the time—the view of the information world from my vantage point is just a blur. Not only is it destined to speed up, but it is also guaranteed to blow our mind along the way, just as the fax machine did to me in the '80s.

Putting Technology in Its (Proper) Place

I love what technology has done to improve our proficiency with medicine, cars, research, and communication, putting boundless information at our fingertips. My concern is the lack of awareness about its effects and the lack of guidance on how to regulate our mobile obsession to counterbalance the dangers.

Children today seem to be born with computer-awareness DNA, ready to compute whatever we put in front of them. Hand a child a cell phone and watch her school you on how it works before she can even read! This can be advantageous. However, parents must be sure to monitor the usage of cell phones and computers in the early stages of a child's development. For a child to have a healthy experience with other humans and physical objects, she needs face-to-face time with both people and playthings.

Moderation doesn't just apply to children. Adults, young adults in particular, live in a globally connected world where multitasking is the norm—and this happens daily in cars while people are driving. According to a 2017 study of hundreds of thousands of drivers, phone distraction was involved in 52 percent of all accidents.[1] People feel pressure to remain in constant contact, day and night, and even when behind the wheel.

The only thing that separates potentially helpful technology from harmful technology is having enough restraint to regulate your usage. By that, I am not speaking about industry or government regulation—I'm talking about your ability to regulate your personal choices. This includes developing the ability to disconnect from technology periodically throughout the day, especially in situations that could be life-threatening to you and others.

I am writing this while sitting in a hotel room in Dublin, Ireland, with internet connectivity issues and spotty to no access to the rest of the world. Believe me, it takes some reconditioning, but I must say it is a relief to have an excuse to separate from my technology tether.

If technology usage goes unregulated, I fear that a type of "electronic obesity" or overuse will grow and worsen as a threat as time passes. I recently saw a mother standing while feeding dinner to her ten-year-old son as he was glued to a computer game. She said it's the only way to make sure that he eats in the evening. Let's be clear: most of us love technology and the benefits it offers. I use it daily just like everyone else, but I am concerned about the stories I hear of how individuals are stressing out and even burning out on technology.

Brain Function and Stress

To better understand technostress, we need to understand how our brain functions and how our body normally responds to the brain's reaction to stimuli. David Perlmutter, MD, a board-certified neurologist, has spent his life studying the brain and the four specific areas of the brain that impact everyday thoughts and actions.[2] His findings divide the brain into four separate and independent segments: the reptilian brain, the limbic system, the neocortex, and the prefrontal cortex.

The reptilian brain is primarily driven by survival instincts. This "survival brain" regulates autonomic computations, including the fight-or-flight response, body temperature, heart rate, and breathing. This ancient aspect of our brain is a reactionary center, casting aside logic to help us stay alive at all costs.

The limbic system consists of the amygdala, hippocampus, and hypothalamus. This is the instinctive emotional center, also considered the "mammalian brain." The limbic system is responsible for appetite control, defensive response, sexuality, and fear.

The neocortex is responsible for writing, speech, computing, and higher-level thinking. The thalamus, a small structure within the neocortex that has extensive nerve connections, signals emotions such as worry, excitement, and joy. This relay signal system can also send concerns to the neocortex to be contemplated, thus producing thoughts and related behaviors.

The prefrontal cortex is responsible for inventing, reasoning, music, science, and creative thinking. It is our link to the future and to overall enlightenment, subscribing to the ancient answers of the past since our own self-interest and self-development are triggered in this brain. It also influences artistic expression and a natural survival function (different from the reptilian brain) related to moderating social behavior. Since this brain region is considered to be where we orchestrate thoughts and actions in accordance with internal goals, it is linked to our cycles of daily activity.

The Evolution of Brain Function

Until the development of technology, our brain operated one way: via simplistic, linear thought processing. Now we are being asked to evolve to accommodate what is essentially a very different type of information interface, running at rapid speeds—and our brains are struggling to adjust. It is like the RAM speed of our newly developing computing mind is overpowering our old hard drive, thus slowing down overall operating performance.

We have all experienced the frustration of a lagging computer that we expect to be lightning fast. The evolutionary process of our brain is not so different. We, too, can experience an overload of information and struggle to concentrate. While we might have sharp recall of short-term memories, our mind is fighting distractions much like a brain that suffers from ADHD.

In reality, our brain's adaptability is remarkable—as witnessed when a person has a stroke and needs for the brain to remap itself. My dad suffered several strokes in his later years, and each time, with guided therapy, he was able to regain speech and movement. This process whereby the brain rewires neural networks to accommodate a new and desired communication of networking flow is called *neuroplasticity.* However, for neuroplasticity to occur, there must be a commitment to the specific repetition of certain movements coupled with focused attention. If either of these elements is missing, the building of a successful neural network superhighway will fail.[3]

Think of it like a massive traffic jam during rush hour on a highway without enough lanes. Frustrated drivers can breed more road rage and, as such, not only delay desired arrival times but also distract us from our focus. The end result of unfocused thinking and lack of concentration is that brain connections are not made and memory is not stored. This leaves the prefrontal cortex overloaded, confused, and incapable of sorting information.[4] On the other hand, when the lanes are open and we are moving freely without disruption, focusing and concentrating on our destination, we are rewarded with emotions such as comfort, satisfaction, and fulfillment. All of this equates to a personal victory in our mind. The data is stored, and the prefrontal cortex can rest and take in new information.

The important thing to remember is that if you want to learn something new, you've got to give it your undivided, concentrated attention while doing it. Otherwise, you will not learn and you will leave your prefrontal cortex overwhelmed and struggling to do all its other jobs.

Therefore, a key ingredient to managing stress when it comes to learning about and using technology is giving it focused, concentrated attention for short periods of time. Don't try to do other things (like writing, driving, or cooking) when you are using technology; you will only create more stress for yourself and others.

Who Is in Charge Here—You or Technology?

With technology becoming more advanced and pervasive, we are in danger of becoming slaves to it. Not only do we deal with poor posture and resultant back pain, we can also suffer from eye strain, chronic headaches, carpal tunnel syndrome or tendonitis from using the mouse too much, and an inability to focus on life tasks.

Working longer hours usually means sitting at our desk slouched over our laptop, which exacerbates poor posture. Just like the alignment of a vehicle is essential for its proper function, posture is also essential to our well-being. Proper posture keeps our muscles, joints, and ligaments in correct alignment, which keeps our vital organs in alignment and functioning effectively. When we don't have proper posture and our body is not aligned, we will eventually develop pain. That pain can actually worsen our posture. However, when we correct our posture with exercise and other therapies, we are promoting easier and deeper breathing, improved circulation and digestion, and a healthier spine.

So how do we keep pace with changes in technology while handling its associated stress and maintaining a measure of wellness? The brief answer to this question is: by learning to regulate technology throughout our day while fully understanding its benefits as well as the challenges. Technology is simply another form of gravity, and if we want to thrive in life, we will need to learn how to see it as good stress.

A New Day Has Dawned

Ever since home computers became widely available in the 1980s, a plethora of other technology has developed. Back then we had simple desktop computers, floppy disks, and fax machines; now we have laptops, smartphones, wireless printers, wireless earbuds, electronic books, smart speakers, and apps for just about everything. Technology has exploded—and we are struggling to keep up.

Technostress has been studied since the mid-1980s. Because of this expanding and intensifying form of gravity, we now have an unknown factor related to how we process and handle stress altogether. If you are experiencing leakage in terms of technostress, you can be sure it is affecting other areas of your life. So it is not something that can be ignored.

There are three important aspects to understanding and properly utilizing technology: *educational awareness, navigation,* and *adaptation. Educational awareness* of the healthy use of technology is sorely lacking. It is just in the past few years that articles and research have begun to appear about the hazardous use of technology.[5]

We have laws in many states—such as those banning cell phones while driving—to prevent damage related to technology use. But what about the activities that we think may be nonhazardous, such as sitting at the computer for most of the day or opting for online social groups rather than spending time face-to-face with people? The extent to which technology affects us is vast, and as a nation, we are just beginning to catch up on needed education to support people in making wiser choices.

Next, we have the challenge of *navigation*. As with anything in life, navigation is an art form. This is especially the case with technology, because it is necessary for connecting with the world on a daily basis. Like the pilot of a plane or driver of a car, we are constantly making adjustments to external conditions for some modicum of enjoyment or safety. However, with technology, most of us are unaware of how stress may be affecting us, which increases the risk of burnout.

In my work with world-renowned race car drivers, I talk a lot about the need to stay aware and awake in order to prevent danger and ensure a safe journey. Two aspects of stress I speak about frequently are our stress response and relaxation response (recovery of expended energy). These two elements happen to be critical in the healthy use of technology.

Technology can provoke a hyperarousal state, speeding up our brain transition and energy expenditure. This is the rush we experience when surfing the web or posting on social media. But like food, too much is simply too much. Since we don't feel the same kind of fullness from technology that we feel with food, we can err on the side of overuse. Next thing we know, we are facing burnout in addition to general body tension, pinched nerves, and more.

The relaxation response is a hypoarousal state, which can be achieved through such methods as meditation, neuromuscular relaxation, rest, and sleep. Sadly, most of us spend too much time with technology during the day, which leaves us at a deficit—feeling strung out and stressed out—by the end of the day. And since we are moving and oscillating less, our mind and body become even more depleted, making us anxious, depressed, distracted, isolated, and sleep-deprived. Learning how to navigate the mental, emotional, spiritual, and physical gravity of technology is necessary if we expect to perform under pressure and thrive in life.

Lastly, we must adapt. *Adaptation* is the ongoing process of assessing the tradeoff of technology in our lives: how much does technology help us versus how much stress does it create? As with every new form of gravity, there is an adjustment period. During this time, we need to pay close attention to stress symptoms, or leakage, in order to function properly. If we do not adapt or align in all areas, we will run short on fuel, alertness, creativity, and innovation.

Measuring Technostress

In recent years, numerous studies have been conducted to measure anxiety, attitudes, and thoughts/feelings about digital technology. The bottom line is that the vast majority of us are feeling the effects of overstimulation. We love our technology, but we are exhausted by it.

The following survey includes statements that address general attitudes and actions toward technology. Circle the number that describes your level of agreement (strongly disagree, disagree, neutral, agree, or strongly agree) with each statement. The important point is for you to begin to get an idea of your relationship with technology and where it could be a source of leakage.

Technostress Survey	
(RATING SCALE: 1=STRONGLY DISAGREE, 5=STRONGLY AGREE)	
I check my phone or social media account throughout the day.	1 2 3 4 5
I communicate with friends and family onscreen most of the time.	1 2 3 4 5
I look at my phone when I'm spending time with other people.	1 2 3 4 5
I look at my phone right before I go to bed.	1 2 3 4 5
I use my phone while driving.	1 2 3 4 5
I answer texts and emails right away, even nonurgent ones.	1 2 3 4 5
I surf the web when I should be working.	1 2 3 4 5
I check my work email on nights and weekends.	1 2 3 4 5
My boss or coworkers text me about nonurgent things during my "off time."	1 2 3 4 5
I mostly use my personal cell phone as my work phone.	1 2 3 4 5
I have lost friends because of things posted on social media.	1 2 3 4 5
Social media has changed my relationships with some people.	1 2 3 4 5
I compare my social life, relationships, appearance, and material possessions to other people's online.	1 2 3 4 5

I feel left out or get depressed because of what I see on social media.	1 2 3 4 5
I have felt bullied or intimidated by people online.	1 2 3 4 5
I'm often upset by online discussions of politics, religion, and current events.	1 2 3 4 5
I am concerned about the effect technology is having on my children.	1 2 3 4 5
I don't know how to manage my children's online activity.	1 2 3 4 5
I worry about protecting my private information online.	1 2 3 4 5
I have seen graphic images online that have disturbed me.	1 2 3 4 5
I spend too much money or buy things impulsively online.	1 2 3 4 5
I get overwhelmed by the amount of information available on the internet.	1 2 3 4 5
I avoid using certain programs, like Excel or PowerPoint.	1 2 3 4 5
I struggle with issues like losing data, formatting documents, or getting locked out of important accounts.	1 2 3 4 5
I can't keep up with all the new apps, updates, and changes to technology.	1 2 3 4 5

If many of your answers fall in the "strongly agree" or "agree" categories, technology may be having a serious impact on your stress levels. Here are tips for handling technostress and producing helpful and healthy reactions:

- Regulate exposure to technical devices. If you work at a computer all day, make sure to take frequent breaks that do not include technology. For example, take a walk outside or visit with colleagues in the break room, but leave all technology, including your phone, behind. Breaking from technology with another form of technology is not ideal, and it won't produce the results you are looking for in terms of recovery.
- Intentionally interact with people face-to-face and by telephone

without the use of social media. Pick up the phone and let them hear your voice. Interacting without social media keeps us tuned in to ourselves and others, which is critical for dealing with gravity and performing well under pressure.

- Power down technology a minimum of thirty minutes, and ideally one hour, before bedtime. Doing so will increase your rest and sleep quality. This means no television, computers, or phones. Read, do yoga, meditate, talk with a loved one, or participate in a hobby that doesn't require technology.
- If you need help minimizing your screen time, try a social media detox. Delete the social media apps from your phone, and try to go a month without using Facebook, Instagram, Snapchat, and Twitter.
- Don't use more than one device at a time. If you're watching TV, put down your phone. If you're working on the computer, stay off your phone and social media.
- If technology is not cooperating with you and causing more harm than good, try "oscillating": get up for a few minutes, take a break, breathe, and then come back to your desk.

PERFORMANCE-BOOSTING STRATEGIES

1. How do you rate your overall relationship with technology and potential areas for improvement? How can you learn to better navigate your technological stresses, or create alignment daily, while still working to be productive and profitable?
2. Consider visiting someone in less fortunate circumstances than you, make intentional eye contact when engaging with someone today, or leave a voicemail for someone to express what that person means to you.

CHAPTER 9

Creating Inspired Change

"It's not an accident that musicians become musicians and engineers become engineers: it's what they're born to do. If you can tune into your purpose and really align with it, setting goals so that your vision is an expression of that purpose, then life flows much more easily."

Jack Canfield, author and motivational speaker

When we achieve the kind of alignment as described in this quote by Jack Canfield, we produce and live out the very purpose that we were put on this planet to enjoy and experience.

When most of us think about alignment, we think about our car. When our car is in alignment, the wheels are completely balanced. The car operates well, with even wear on the brakes and tires. When it is out of alignment, our car won't run optimally. It may "pull" to one side, and the brakes and tires will wear unevenly. If left uncorrected for a period of time, the car may start to shake or vibrate. Eventually, we will have some sort of a breakdown.

The same goes for us, but in our case, our "wheels" are our mental, emotional, spiritual, and physical areas. When we have alignment in all of these areas, we are running well, better able to manage stress and perform under pressure.

I have had several BMWs in my life. Not only are these incredible cars, but I also happen to really like their brand slogan "The ultimate driving machine," because it relates well to performance and life mastery. If you watch BMW commercials closely, you will recognize that they are not just promoting the quality of the car. What they are promoting is the quality of life as an owner of a BMW. The marketers want you to know that there is an exciting, purposeful journey that awaits when you drive a BMW—and not just the journey from point A to point B, but also the journey inside and outside the car.

These companies invest millions of dollars each year to deliver purposeful messages to get you to purchase their products. But while they may guide you toward an experience, ultimately you are responsible for defining and creating your own experiences with any product that you buy—or buy into.

This concept of creating your own experience is even truer for life itself. Since life is a form of gravity, you can either let life's circumstances define you or you can determine how you are going to live your life. You are, in essence, given an "ultimate driving machine" (your body, mind, and spirit), as well as guidance (through friends, family, mentors, and coaches) toward experiences that will enhance your life. But you are the one who creates your experience of life day-to-day. It's that simple.

In one real sense, life is about creating the most enjoyable and memorable moments day after day, month after month, and year after year. Over time, these moments become the "motion picture" of your life, with you as the main character along with a host of supporting cast members. If you viewed your life this way, what actions would you prioritize daily? What would you think, say, and do to create the most authentic and best possible movie about *you*?

I go to movies to experience a range of emotions—from sadness to joy, inspiration to exhilaration. My hope is to have a total mind/body/spirit connection with the storyline and script. I'm "all in" from the beginning of a movie. I want to feel as if I am experiencing life from the vantage point of the characters on the screen.

Unlike the movies, however, I do not just watch my life unfold, with no influence on the outcome. If there is a "scene" I am not happy with, I have the ability to influence the direction of it. Sometimes I can change the scene or write a new one. Other times I can alter how my "character" reacts to the scene, which can impact the outcome of the "movie." With my life, I'm able to create different outcomes through my actions and attitudes.

My intent is to share with you the practices I know that work to create peak performance. This way, you can begin working to achieve your goal to live the life of your dreams.

In the previous chapters, we looked at many aspects of our human makeup. If you have completed the exercises at the end of each chapter, you've learned a lot about yourself—your strengths, weaknesses, dreams, wishes, hopes, and desires. Hopefully, you have some idea of how strong, flexible, and resilient you are. You have also learned more about your body, including which activities invigorate you and which ones deplete you. Plus, you have some idea of the gravity in your life and how it affects you, as well as the thoughts that might be causing you stress or holding you back. You may even know what is needed to create new rituals in your life.

The purpose of this chapter is to help you take all this information and create inspired change. By following the process outlined here, you will find out how to take the next step and learn how to perform well under pressure.

The 4-Step Process of Inspired Change

The Life Mastery Pyramid is a visual I've created to show what happens when you experience gravity/stress. You can let gravity get you down (as shown at the bottom of the pyramid), and you can stay there by holding on to old habits, or you can release those habits and work to help develop healthy rituals—thus moving up the pyramid to create inspired change.

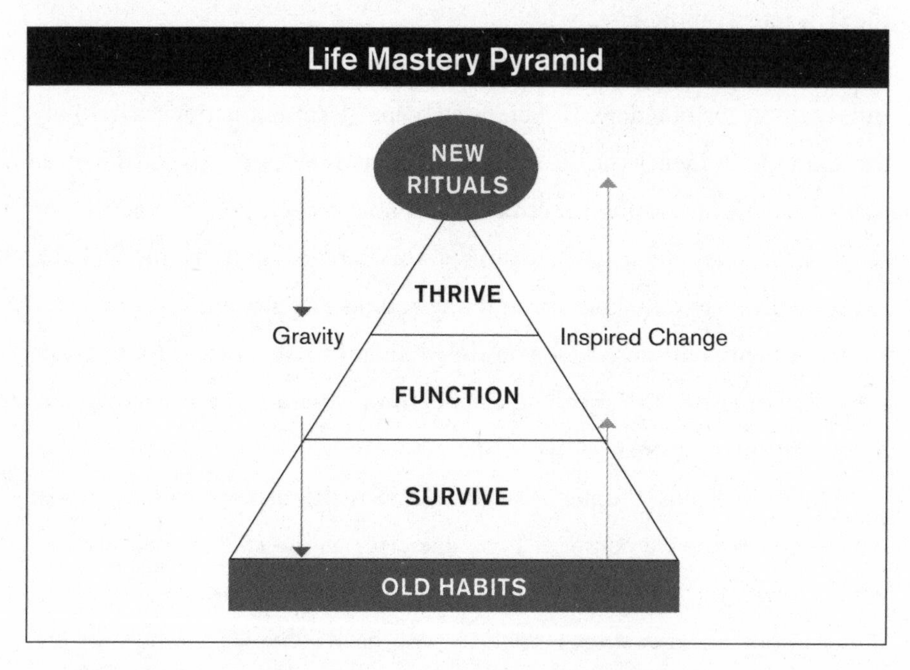

As you spend more of your time on new habits, you will create an upwardly mobile vortex, which brings you to higher levels on the pyramid. People who train themselves to move up the pyramid work their way into a life where they are thriving. On the other hand, if you allow gravity to push you down into old, unhelpful habits, you will only live in survival or function modes.

So how exactly do we create a life of new rituals? It's a fairly simple practice, once you get the hang of it, even if it's not always easy.

If you want to move to the top of the Life Mastery Pyramid—from *survive* to *thrive*—you must follow the 4-Step Process of Inspired Change. Assessing your current relationship to each of these steps is critical to understanding where you want to focus your training.

The 4-Step Process of Inspired Change includes the following elements:

Step 1: Identify

As I've stated throughout the book, gravity is stress and stress is gravity. They are one and the same, neither good nor bad. They are just situations, circumstances, occurrences, or persons requiring our attention.

The key practices for this first part of the 4-Step Process are:

Develop Recognition/Awareness. Begin by developing awareness so you can pick up on situations that require your attention. This step requires slowing down enough to become highly conscious of your thoughts and actions, as well as your emotions. It is through the process of recognition that you begin to gauge your reactions and responses to situations, determining what is right for you and what is not. It is also the process where you see clearly the behaviors or habits that are working for you or working against you. Without awareness, no change is possible.

Change Your Perception. This is the stage where you refuse to allow yourself to believe that what is happening is "bad." If you see something as bad, you will see what is happening as a threat and will deal with it accordingly. This will not produce the outcome you desire, as it will be fear-based. Actions prompted by fear keep you trapped at the bottom of the pyramid at the survival level. Instead, if you see gravity as a challenge rather than a setback, you will address it as an opportunity for growth and expansion.

These are some of the statements you can reflect on to help you identify how well positioned you are to handle gravity:

- I am great at recognizing when I am stressed, angry, or upset.
- I am comfortable with my feelings and don't push them down when they arise.
- Once I see what needs changing, I feel excited about changing it.
- There are always areas where I could become better, and I can easily identify what those are.
- I know what is best for me and what is not. When I see something that needs to be changed, I start working toward the change that I want to see.

Bottom line: to become proficient at step 1, you must learn to welcome your thoughts and emotions. From there, you can work to cultivate an attitude that whatever comes along is for your benefit—it is an opportunity to learn more about yourself and move closer to what you want in life.

Step 2: Process

In the second step of the 4-Step Process of Inspired Change, you look at your old habits and sort out the weeds, so to speak, from the grass. Here, you take an inventory of the habits that may have contributed to the current situation or crisis. In this stage, you also look at what change you *really* want to make and why. Here are the key practices:

Create a mock crisis. In the mock crisis, you want to connect to the worst-case scenario related to the situation by asking, "What path am I headed down if I continue this behavior?" It is crucial to sit with and fully experience the feelings that come up, rather than just examine them intellectually. This will get you in touch with the true gravity of the situation.

Clarify why you want to change. For change to be lasting, it must be internally driven versus externally motivated. You cannot sustain change that is not authentic to you; you simply will not be inspired to stay on track. So as you are considering what changes you want to make, also look at your underlying motivation. Get clear on why you want to change.

Cultivate your vision of success. Once you get clear on what it is you really want, take some time to begin to cultivate your vision of success. Envision what you will look and feel like as you make the change—and what your life will look and feel like upon achieving the goal. Do not shortchange yourself on this step; it is the step that provides the fuel to change. Cut out inspiring images from magazines and make a vision board; surf the internet and read about other people who have what you want; change your screen saver to reflect what you desire. Do whatever it takes to get yourself charged up—you will need it for the journey.

Here are some statements for step 2 that you can reflect on to identify how well positioned you are for handling the process:

- I feel ________________ when I consider the worst-case scenario.
- I'm really "done" with this behavior; I will do anything to achieve a new reality.
- I feel excited about achieving this goal.
- This change comes from my core values; it is something that I fully resonate with.
- I am ready to transform habits into new rituals. I feel confident that I can do it.

Bottom line: to become proficient at step 2, you need to allow yourself to go deeply into the worst-case scenario and play it out. If you cannot really envision the crisis, you will not change. Remember, even though humans are programmed for stress, we are *not* programmed for change. Most people hate change. We crave constancy, predictability, and comfort. In most cases, we will wait for a real crisis to hit before taking action—but by then, it could be too late. This is why the mock crisis is such a valuable tool. Use it well.

Step 3: Plan

In this step, you create and work your plan of action. Step 3 includes specific tools as well as actions toward new rituals that will help you reach your goal. During this time, you also want to identify the barriers that may prevent you from achieving your goal. Here, you stay closely linked to your personal stress code (your areas of leakage, as described in chapter 1) and plan specific practices that will get you to where you want to go.

Remember, working toward achieving a goal is a journey. It's not just about the end goal, but also about enjoying the process. You can work toward a goal, but if you are not calm, centered, and fulfilled, you are not thriving. Focusing on the here and now is critical. When you work toward a goal, you will likely experience doubts and setbacks from time to time. There will be days when you may even question your original goal. This is natural. However, knowing in advance that you will be facing these kinds of situations will help you be better prepared.

Key planning steps are:

Identify your MESP (mental, emotional, spiritual, physical) leakage. Each of us has a key area of leakage. If you don't know what yours is, review the initial set of questions I put forth in chapter 1. This may be an area where you have struggled for many years. You may have more than one area of leakage. In order to crack your personal stress code, you need to know which areas you struggle most in—because these are the areas where the breakdowns will occur first.

Patch one area of leakage. In order to change a particular behavior or create a new ritual of any kind, you must take specific actions that will support you in breaking your old habits and creating new ones. These actions should be done daily for at least thirty to forty-five days. (The process of identifying and patching core areas of leakage is covered in more detail in chapter 10.)

Remember your mock crisis. This is the practice of remembering *why* you are doing what you are doing. Use this practice whenever you feel uncertain, skeptical, or down. Think about your worst-case scenario for several minutes until you can remember why you decided to embark upon the change in the first place.

Utilize inspirational pictures daily. As I noted in step 2, visual images are crucial for us to create inspired change. In just seconds, pictures can put you in an inspired place; they can also remind you of your "why" and keep you connected to your purpose in life.

Flip a coin. I use a "Threat/Challenge Coin" with the people I coach to help them transition from negative and toxic thoughts, emotions, beliefs, and behaviors to positive beliefs and actions. The tail side of the coin shows a picture of a thunderstorm with the words "Bad Stress/Threat." The head side of the coin shows a picture of a person rock climbing with the words "Good Stress/Challenge." Anything viewed as a threat becomes bad stress, but converting that potential threat with the simple flip of the coin can produce a challenge response, or good stress.

In sports, viewing stress as competition allows athletes to move to a more favorable (winning) outcome. The coin provides a powerful way to become more self-aware and accountable for your daily thoughts and actions and helps empower you during transitional life stress.

For example, if your "threat" is the stress of being in a toxic job, the "challenge" response might be to find a job in a more positive environment. This exercise can be done several ways: verbally, by stating the threat ("I'm afraid I'll lose my job") and then the challenge out loud ("I will find better options for work"); mentally, by picturing a coin as it flips from a threat (possible unemployment) to a challenge response (better pay with a supportive boss); or physically, by creating and flipping your own "coin" as you process your thoughts and emotions related to your job.

Use the Threat/Challenge Coin to help you remember the truth about gravity, or stress. Remember, gravity is always present. The key is to flip your perspective and view stress as an opportunity.

Commit to action—and practice correctly. I put these concepts together because they remind me of this popular quote attributed to football coach Vince Lombardi: "Practice does not make perfect; perfect practice makes perfect." If you want to reach your goal, you've got to practice correctly and regularly. Committed action means employing a "no matter what" attitude and necessitates daily engagement until the new ritual becomes automatic.

These statements for step 3 can help you reflect on how well positioned you are for handling the plan:

- Once I put my mind to something, nothing can stop me.
- I have several consistent practices in my life.
- It is becoming easier for me to see stress as good.
- I have a number of inspirational pictures to remind me of what I most want in life right now.
- Once I start a new practice, I keep it up easily.

Bottom line: to become proficient at step 3, you need to form a great relationship with practice *and* with learning. In truth, we are all practicing becoming better at something—whether a better parent, partner, or businessperson. We will not be perfect in our endeavors; there's no sense in trying to be. That just creates more stress. Instead, we must be kind to ourselves and others as we take on new habits.

Step 4: Thrive

This step is about becoming comfortable with your new rituals and the levels you reach in the Life Mastery Pyramid. As you get better at creating inspired change, you will reach ever-increasing heights on the pyramid. Eventually, all that you do will be supercharged. You will have found your thrive. This does not mean you will never feel sad, fearful, or angry, but you will be able to process these emotions quickly and effectively. You will also have an easier time recognizing old habits in need of transformation, as well as signs of leakage. But at this level, you will be so practiced at your new way of living and being that everything will become easier.

Let's take a look at a few of the key practices and reminders for this step.

When you are operating in a thrive state, you will become . . .

Comfortable in your new skin. When you develop a new ritual, it seems odd at first. It takes time and practice for it to become your norm and for you to feel comfortable with it. Fortunately, by the time you reach the thrive stage, your new rituals have become ingrained—part of you and your daily routine.

Tuned into your recovery needs. At this stage, you are so tuned into the need for breaks that your body starts to let you know when it's ready. After a while, you will not need to set an alarm for breaks. You will take them naturally. Until that happens, though, set the alarm! You cannot thrive without regular oscillation.

Aligned for recovery. When you first practice alignment, it is typically because you have fallen off track. Once you reach your thrive state, your MESP alignment practice becomes second nature—so much so that it can be used as an activity of recovery. In this case, it can inspire you in a moment.

Tough—strong, flexible, and resilient. As you work your way up the Life Mastery Pyramid, you will gain toughness. You build toughness—a combination of strength, flexibility, and resiliency—when you can appropriately reframe failures in combination with compassionate persistence. In this thrive state, toughness is not about forcing or getting your way; instead, it is having the maturity to realize that you are in a flow with life and therefore need to remain flexible and present. Toughness will enable you to handle the inevitable shifts and changes that occur while you are working toward your goals. It may even result in you changing a particular goal or reprioritizing your goals.

Connected to your purpose. Our purpose is connected to a drive that we have had toward something for most of our lives—our reason for being here. It has to do with service toward others, since this is a key component of living a healthy life. People who thrive connect daily to their purpose for being here and allow that to drive their thoughts and actions.

These statements for step 4 will help you determine how well positioned you are to thrive:

- I know my purpose for being here, and I live it every day.
- I take frequent breaks and feel refreshed after most of them.
- It is becoming easier for me to perform my new rituals.
- I wouldn't change much about my life; I love my life.
- What people say doesn't bother me much anymore; I am clear about who I am and what I want in this world.

Bottom line: finding your thrive requires you to make a consistent effort to work at the practices outlined above. It also takes failure, which builds confidence, clarity, and life toughness. People who thrive are typically honest about their weaknesses. In addition to having compassionate persistence, thriving people aren't afraid of their leakages; they have patched many of them and are ready, willing, and able to step up and patch more when necessary.

The 4-Step Process of Inspired Change will change the way you experience stress. When you are letting gravity bring you down, the stress is heavier than when you are working through the steps to move up the pyramid. There is stress throughout the process of inspired change, but as you become proficient at overcoming gravity, your stress will become mostly related to discomfort around the unknown. As you move up the pyramid, your life will change: your income and sphere of influence may increase, and your job and friends may change.

Having a mentor or coach is recommended for anyone who wants to thrive in life. This person will help you navigate unknown territory by sharing their experiences with you and offering support in all sorts of ways.

What to Do When You Get Stuck

Now let's do an exercise. Think of a goal that you have not achieved. Where are you in the 4-Step Process of Inspired Change? Are you experiencing some difficulty in how you perceive or process the gravity or the emotions related to it? Are you struggling with old habits, possibly believing that you cannot change an old habit, or that you have too many bad habits? Perhaps you are working toward inspired change, but you lost interest or got distracted shortly after embarking on the change. Again, it does not matter where you tend to stall in this cycle; the key is to tie into your core wound and primary area of leakage.

In fact, what matters is that you have a sense of where you get stuck. As I alluded to before, with awareness and a commitment to work through these roadblocks, you will achieve a new set point from which your experience of life will improve dramatically. And here's the good news: the only thing that you need to do when you get stuck is to create alignment. That is all. So, ultimately, moving up the Life Mastery Pyramid has everything to do with practicing alignment over and over again. Alignment helps you to eliminate harmful stress so you can achieve your goals.

Sometimes we find ourselves thriving in one aspect of the cycle, only to be suddenly kicked backward to another stage. The trick here is to know in advance that we are never done learning and evolving. Just because we overcome one bad habit doesn't mean that others won't appear. Becoming your best self involves knowing that the experience of change and development is a form of gravity itself. It is a natural part of the journey.

We are creative and complex beings with an endless stream of desires, along with a potential boatload of mental and emotional nuances to be dealt with on a daily basis. We also don't operate in a bubble. We must have some basic level of cooperation with the outer world in order to thrive.

How Much Time Does It Take, Really?

Lots of people I train ask me how much time it takes to master your stress and reach a thriving state. My answer is always the same, and it's twofold: "You don't ever get done" and "It depends." Let me explain. First, in reality, you are never "done with" stress. What you become done with is your struggle against it; instead, you learn how to thrive with it. Each of us will always deal with gravity, throughout our entire lives.

Second, you can achieve such a high level of proficiency with inspired change that stress doesn't weigh you down very much. In this case, you have fully accepted the realities of *life as stress*. And because you do not have an adverse relationship with your weaknesses and with gravity, you experience far more lightness and enjoyment overall. Yes, you can permanently shift your relationship with stress and be free from its harmful effects.

The time it takes to reach this state can depend on several things, but there is one key factor in all of this—*the degree to which you are aware of and want to do something about your suffering.* None of us can escape the pain of existence; it is a fact of life. We lose people close to us. We get downsized from jobs or suffer financial loss. We falter because of our weaknesses and failures. But we also tend to add suffering to the pain by telling ourselves that what is happening is "wrong" or "bad." We tell ourselves the situation cannot be changed, or, even worse, that there is something wrong with us. We might become so inflexible in our beliefs that we become hardened and chronically angry. To numb the pain, we may turn to a substance, like alcohol or drugs, or an activity, like eating, gambling, or shopping. These are just a few examples of how we create even more suffering from pain.

If you learn how to become friendly toward stress, however, you will begin to consistently evaluate what happens in life as just "what is." Then you have the chance to transform the pain of "what is" into inspired living. Because the mind will stubbornly resist this notion, you need to practice flipping the Threat/Challenge coin all day long, day in and day out, until you have built a new neural pathway and your mind automatically begins to equate stress with opportunity. Until you get good at this, you won't be in charge of creating your life experience; instead, gravity will be dictating your feelings and your moods. As a general rule, flipping the coin is easier when you are not dealing with a crisis. But even in a crisis, you can learn to manage your emotions if you are persistent.

A few years ago, I was visiting one of my clients, race car driver Doug Herbert, at the track. Doug is a National Hot Rod Association (NHRA) and International Hot Rod Association (IHRA) champion. He was preparing for a practice drive when his phone rang. He answered the phone, and within seconds he was on the ground sobbing.

He had just received word that his two young sons—twelve and seventeen years old—had been instantly killed in a car accident. The gravity of this situation was overwhelming. Doug was not only in shock, but he was also in the midst of deep despair and immediate, almost interminable grief.

Understandably, Doug's deep sorrow continued for months. Although he continued to drive, the grief of the situation was paralyzing, and he had lost his zest for life. Meanwhile, I was working to help Doug focus on what he could be grateful for in this tragedy. Some days, this was more difficult than others. Then one day, I received a call from him.

"Terry, I don't want to race anymore," he told me. "I want to create a driving school for teens so I can teach young people how to deal with difficult driving situations. With the school, maybe I can help save the lives of young children."

Doug went on to found B.R.A.K.E.S., which stands for "Be Responsible and Keep Everyone Safe," a nonprofit organization headquartered in Charlotte, North Carolina. I knew in that moment that he had found his way through the gravity of the situation and out the other side. He was now in the beginning stages of inspired change—embarking up the Life Mastery Pyramid.

Did this take time? Yes. Lots of time. But if we allow ourselves the time to process—even when the pain of life becomes so great that we'd rather die—we can overcome anything.

A Commitment to Thrive

The survival rung on the pyramid is a painful place to be, either in the short run or over the long haul. Survival implies struggle, and with struggle comes stress.

Nonetheless, the bottom line regarding any change is this: *you must be actively committed, every day, to mastering your stress.* Only people who are committed to thriving will be able to overcome the inertia created by gravity; otherwise, they will fall prey to compensatory habits related to leakage. Let me give you a personal example.

One thing that I was clear about as a young man was that not trying to live my destiny was more painful than trying and failing. This enabled me to create the 4 Steps of Inspired Change (Identify, Process, Plan, and Thrive) and actively live by them. I knew by doing this it would become obvious what my purpose and destiny was in life. And in time, it did.

There were times when I got stuck and there would be leakage. Back then, my Achilles' heel was spiritual leakage—I had an outdated belief system about life, how it should be, and what was possible. For example, I'd grown up believing in God, but when our son Brandon was born with severe medical complications, my faith was rocked. During those early years of Brandon's life, I often pleaded with God, asking why He had stricken Brandon with this disease: "Why him? Why me? Why our family?" Eventually, the persistence of this story and the pain that it created for me was enough to wake me up and cause me to choose a different belief system, one that helped me feel good about life again. When I shifted my belief system—from believing I was a victim to believing that God could help me find good in my circumstances—everything changed. I began telling myself, "God would never give me something I couldn't handle, and this is His way of shining His glory through both Brandon and me."

I became instantly inspired to create something good out of the bad that I was perceiving and that was weighing me down. My life changed radically. I was suddenly aligned spiritually, and my mental, emotional, and physical alignment followed quickly. I had more energy, my mental clarity was back, and my emotions dissipated. This crisis, as well as my realization of what my life would be like if I didn't change, truly propelled me forward.

Over time, with awareness, I stopped getting stuck as much in that one place. That didn't mean I never got stuck again. Of course I did, but I always knew where to look first—specifically to the "Why me? Why him?" belief. You see, even if we have an epiphany about something, it does not mean that those old habitual ways of thinking or acting don't return. They do; the weeds are always there. It simply becomes easier to pull them and return our focus to the present moment and to what we are creating.

We only have the present moment. The future is a product of our imagination. If you want to learn to thrive under pressure, the best chance you have to do this is to start right now. The choices we make today shape our future; it really is this basic. But we often think that there is magic to this—that somehow, we will mysteriously handle life better tomorrow even though we aren't handling it well today. This couldn't be further from the truth! If you want a better tomorrow, create a better today and then tomorrow will take care of itself.

Finally, you must *anticipate* that you will be able to thrive under pressure but not *expect* it. I know this sounds strange, but there is a big difference between these concepts. Too many people become consumed by an end goal, inadvertently creating misery in the form of extra stress for themselves and others through obsessive thoughts like, "When is it going to happen?" Remember, stress never goes away, so be your success now and don't worry so much about the future. Instead of worrying, anticipate that you will succeed. Anticipation is a much sweeter place to live and reside. This way, you can be confidently, diligently practicing away. Over time, with patient practice, you will enjoy big leaps in progress, reaching new levels on the Life Mastery Pyramid.

PERFORMANCE-BOOSTING STRATEGIES

1. Recognize the difference between alignment and balance.

Alignment is directional and balance is positional. Consider where you are going while thinking about the Life Mastery Pyramid.

2. Start every morning with an alignment thought. For example, I like to ask myself, "What is *important* versus what is *urgent* today?"

CHAPTER 10

Cracking Your Personal Stress Code

"It's not the load that breaks you down, it's the way you carry it."
Attributed to Lou Holtz, legendary football coach

We all have a personal stress code—a specific mix of tolerances and intolerances based on our life experiences and perspectives, and our strengths and weaknesses. The key to thriving under pressure is identifying and unlocking your own stress code and using it to transform your relationship with stress/gravity.

To identify your stress code, you need to first determine in which of the four aspects of human development—mental, emotional, spiritual, or physical—you consistently experience the most leakage. You are looking for your core wound that, essentially, continuously causes the most stress.

How do you find it? The quickest way to determine your personal stress code is to revisit the questionnaire in chapter 1. In which category did you have the lowest score? Now, looking back at that specific category, ask yourself, "What is it that I do, think, believe, or say that consistently causes my energy to cycle down?" It may not come to you right away, but if you ask the question sincerely, the answer will come in time.

Then, write it down somewhere. The more specific you can be, the better. One way of writing it is: "I notice that I do ________________ when ________________ happens." Examples of this could be:

- "I notice that I eat sugar when I feel stressed or tired." (physical leakage)
- "I notice that when someone comments on my work performance, I blame the boss." (emotional leakage)
- "I notice that I'm regularly angry when I see what's happening in our world." (mental leakage)
- "I notice that I don't believe that I deserve good things in life when I fail in some way." (spiritual leakage)

These are all examples of leakage that could color our life experience and cause us to sabotage efforts toward real change. Although we typically have leakage in one predominant area, our leakage often causes the other three areas to be out of balance, too. But it's not as important to identify the category as it is to get clear on the underlying problem. Our job, as I've said, is to dig deep and find the core wound.

It's easy to think of the example "I notice that I eat sugar when I feel stressed or tired" as just physical leakage. It may be. But if the core issue is an underlying anxiety about life, it might be better to classify this leakage as a mental or spiritual issue—even though there may be real physical issues present. The point is that if we address a symptom rather than the core issue, we will not experience sustained change. For example, we could potentially address our overeating by starting a workout regimen. We might lose weight and even start eating more healthfully, but if the underlying issue of anxiety isn't addressed, we will begin to compensate with something other than sugar. (Who knows, we could become an exercise addict!)

Key underlying issues will cause leakage in every area—mental, emotional, physical, and spiritual. But in order to crack your stress code, you'll need to identify your primary area of leakage first; that is the one you'll need to patch right away to start having more success in the 4-Step Process of Inspired Change. If left unpatched, that core leakage will not only affect every other aspect of your life, but it may also cause a complete breakdown.

Patching Your Leakage

So where do you look first? Typically, the origin of the leakage goes back to your core wound, even if you've done work to patch it. By the way, it isn't a good use of energy to try to get rid of your core wound—that is generally futile—nor is it necessary to have a thriving life. What you want to do, instead, is to use the next few steps to reconnect to your inspiration for making the change in the first place. It's a redirection of focus and attention. Any time you notice leakage, you'll want to practice these steps:

Step 1: Mock Crisis

To break an old habit, the supporting behaviors around that habit must first be interrupted with plenty of emotion and passion. This will tip the scale, allowing you to create a healthy, new ritual. A life crisis often produces the emotion and passion to accomplish this exercise. But in the absence of a real crisis, a mock crisis can be used to get the same result. In other words, by completing step 1, the scale can begin to tip in the direction of change. Or, if you have lost your way, revisiting this mock crisis will get you back on track.

As a reminder, connect to the worst-case scenario related to the situation by asking, "What path am I headed down if I continue this behavior?" This will often result in you saying, "Oh, yeah, that is why I'm doing this mock crisis. Now I remember." Fully experience the feelings that come up.

Step 2: MESP Assessment of the *Needs You Are Not Meeting* through the Behavior or Situation

Here, you get in touch with the life needs that you are *not* meeting by continuing to engage in the old habit rather than creating a new ritual. Once you gain clarity about this, it is much easier to remind yourself of what you are missing out on by not making changes. For this process, you can complete an assessment for each MESP (mental, emotional, spiritual, and physical) area or just select your personal stress code (your primary area of leakage) and deal with that.

For example, if my lowest score is in the physical area, I need to make that my focus while harnessing the other three areas to empower the physical. This will create the best possible alignment. As I've mentioned, it is better to focus on *one* area of change first for approximately thirty to forty-five days (or however long it takes) until you've built some level of proficiency toward your new ritual. Without attention and energy to MESP alignment, change is not probable.

Step 3: MESP Assessment of the *Needs You Would Fulfill* by Changing the Behavior or Situation

In this third step, you identify all the needs—mental, emotional, spiritual, and physical—you will be meeting by making the change. Here, you want to use the strongest visuals possible to help you develop new (or renewed) leverage. These can be pictures on a vision board, a list of attributes that you post in your office, or even a compelling mental image. Reference these visuals often to remind yourself why the change is needed and desired. Think about how you will feel, look, and think, and what you will believe about yourself once you have accomplished your goal.

Involve as many senses as possible and take your time with this process—really get into it. This could be a picture of who you were in the past, who you want to become in the future, or even a representation of what success will look like when your goals are met. This sounds simple, but it is effective. It takes incredible attention to focus and gain purposeful alignment to make changes stick. Use every tool possible to get yourself back on track.

Step 4: Evaluation and Adjustment of Practices until the New Ritual Is Internalized

This process involves a couple of steps. The first step is to identify the actions and behaviors in each MESP category that are needed to make the change. The second step is to monitor how successful you are with these supportive actions, tweaking as necessary. Step 4 is all about evaluating and working the plan daily to support the change. It takes work to develop a new ritual, and it takes work to maintain the conditioned change.

Let's say I am now eating a healthier diet and have achieved my optimal weight. I will need to know, daily, when my weight and energy are not at optimal levels. What if I go on vacation and indulge in too many rich foods because I'm eating out more? If I'm checking in daily, I will notice when there is a discrepancy. At this point, I will immediately acknowledge this and go back through the first three steps to realign and reestablish the change process. I must not wait to do this! If I take the time to realign, it will allow me to get back on track by patching the leakage. In this case, if my leakage is physical and I see that my overeating is linked to not exercising,

I will get moving for the remainder of my vacation because I know exercise will help me make better food choices.

Going through all three steps will also fill me with the energy, focus, and passion that I had when the mock crisis or real crisis occurred. So, follow all the steps. If you've fallen away from optimal rituals, you need an equal and/or greater force to bring you back.

This ongoing daily situational awareness will develop into a self-monitored accountability and coaching protocol that will keep you cycling up the pyramid from surviving to thriving. Your fuel is the inspiration that comes from being aligned with your life goals and life purpose. This is the key to sustained change!

Remember, just because you want to change doesn't mean that everything will go smoothly. You will have setbacks or sometimes even false starts, and you need to know exactly how to get back on track. If you have identified an area of change but are unsuccessful at making the change, you will have to contend with additional MESP leakages. Engaging in the alignment process over and over again will help you mitigate the damage and get back on track.

Now that you know how to crack your personal stress code, you can apply these steps to things you want to change in your own life. Here is an example to help you understand how to use this tool while you are working on creating new rituals so that you can perform under every kind of pressure.

Example: Quit Smoking

STEP 1: MOCK CRISIS

If I continue to smoke, I will die at an early age.

STEP 2: MESP NEEDS ASSESSMENT (NEGATIVE OUTCOMES)

Mental—*If I continue to smoke, I will think bad thoughts about myself and continue to beat myself up.*

Emotional—*If I continue to smoke, I will feel disgusted with myself, and I will never find the courage to develop the relationship that I want.*

Spiritual—*If I continue to smoke, I will believe that I am no good and will never ask for the raise that I really believe I deserve.*

Physical—*If I continue to smoke, my teeth will continue to turn brown and decay, and I will need to spend thousands of dollars to fix them.*

STEP 3: MESP NEEDS ASSESSMENT (POSITIVE OUTCOMES)

Mental—*If I stop smoking, I will feel proud of myself and my confidence will soar. I will look and feel better, and people will notice and ask me about it.*

Emotional—*If I stop smoking, I will feel happy with myself for the first time in ten years, and that will help my chances of attracting a new love.*

Spiritual—*If I stop smoking, I will start to believe that I am a good person and that I can face challenges in life and overcome them.*

Physical—*If I stop smoking, I will finally spend the money to whiten my teeth so that they look better. I will also feel more like riding my bike because I won't be so out of breath.*

STEP 4: EVALUATION AND ADJUSTMENT

This process involves evaluating your original MESP behaviors and making the necessary adjustments. If you come out of alignment, the issue is related to some MESP leakage. Once you determine where the leakage is, you can fix it by putting a new action into place and examining your results.

The first step is to identify the specific MESP actions and behaviors that are needed to put the change into action. So if your plan is to quit smoking within three months, you should write down the actions you need to take to actually have this occur:

Mental—*I will write down all of the reasons I am doing this and read them every morning before going to work and every evening before I go to bed. I will post reminders on slips of paper throughout the house about what I will gain by making this change.*

Emotional—*When I feel irritable, vulnerable, or weak, I will call a friend and go for a walk or a bike ride to help with my emotions. I will also make sure that I take up one new hobby as a distraction for when I'm feeling really low during this transition.*

Spiritual—*I will commit to attending the weekly support group at my local health center for people who are quitting smoking. There, I will find new friends I can call on when needed.*

Physical—*I will not go to happy hour on Friday after work for eight weeks until I feel more in control in social settings. Instead, I will join a gym and exercise. I will also be sure to carry chewing gum with me at all times for when I might get cravings, and I'll make plans on Friday night to do something with one of my friends from the support group.*

Once you put these plans into effect, monitor your success levels with them and tweak them as needed. You will want to monitor yourself more vigorously in the early stages of implementation so that you are not tempted to fall back into old behaviors. Remember to focus on your primary area of leakage or weakness for at least thirty to forty-five days. In the example of quitting smoking, if your primary area of weakness is spiritual, use your mental, emotional, and physical energies to support your spiritual side. Make that weekly support group the center of your life for a while. Take walks with group members (physical) and talk to other group members (emotional). See yourself as successful (mental), perhaps even helping other group members.

Change is a constant process of alignment and realignment. If you need help from a counselor or friend, then get it. You may want to tell your friends in advance what you are doing and that you may be calling to ask for their help. You can discuss what that help may look like so that your friends are ready to receive your calls and know how to respond. All of this planning helps to ensure that you will be successful at creating change.

The worst thing to do is to underplan or to underanticipate what the change may entail. This is why getting help from others who have been through your particular type of gravity can be extremely helpful. Those people can give you ideas and guidance that you may not have even considered.

Your life—as it is now and as it could be—is entirely up to you. Gravity can control you, or you can have dominion over it. Which do you think is the least stressful path, ultimately?

PERFORMANCE-BOOSTING STRATEGIES

1. Think about a change you have wanted to make but haven't yet been successful at implementing. Consider your personal stress code as it relates to alignment and how you might mobilize yourself now, with this new understanding, to get back on the cycle of inspired change.
2. Note when and where it is easy for you to remain aligned, and when and where it is difficult. This is called situational awareness, which will help you set yourself up for success. When you know when and where you thrive, you can plan your thirty- to forty-five-day transition to make use of this valuable insight.

CHAPTER 11

Hope Is the Canvas of Life

"Hope is the dream of a soul awake."
French proverb

As we travel through life, we paint the details of our goals, aspirations, and dreams onto the canvas of hope—but these details are merely the colors and the brushstrokes. Without hope, we have nothing to paint on.

The word *hope* has its roots in Old English and German, which give the word an essential meaning of "trust." There is a big distinction here. While we tend to view hope as a gamble or, more cynically, an empty waste of time, the original word suggests none of that uncertainty. Hope is the equivalent of trust, which is the confident expectation of something or someone. When we trust, we rely on the integrity, ability, or character of a person or thing. We trust that everything will work according to our best interest and favored outcome. Hope is not a pie-in-the-sky endeavor. Rather, holding on to hope is a spiritual way to create what we want and need.

Some dictionaries also suggest that hope is connected to the word *hop*, as in taking a leap. When you hope, you take a leap in expectation. Hope is the ultimate exercise in falling forward.

Hope is also the foundation of any healing process, whether mental, emotional, spiritual, or physical. This is especially true of people with physical diseases. The medical establishment will tell you that attitude is a huge part of healing. People's expectations—their hope—powerfully shape how their body responds to disease. Sometimes people spontaneously heal. Couples who have struggled with infertility for years suddenly have a baby. Studies find that the placebo effect is alive and well.[1] People who are given inactive sugar pills for comparison purposes often experience a reduction in symptoms and an improvement in physical or emotional health with no medical intervention. In essence, they believe they are getting better, so they do.

Studies show that individuals who are optimistic, even in the face of chronic illness, live longer and in some cases heal.[2] Magic Johnson has been living with HIV since 1991. He's a living example of mind over matter coupled with good medical treatment. (He also has the advantage of being an elite athlete who has likely mastered his response to stress.)

On the other hand, people who give in to illness, who believe that they'll never beat their disease or think that they can't do anything to make their situation better, often find that their expectations are met. Too often people—whether ill or not—simply give up, give in to life, and settle. They also don't give themselves the opportunity to reach their full potential or to heal from past wounds, whether physical, mental, emotional, or spiritual. They think life has no further fruit to bear. Or it hurts too much to hope for anything better after so much disappointment.

There is a solution to this, but like everything else, it takes work and support. (There is also work involved in maintaining a state of hopelessness, so it's a matter of choosing which stress you would rather have.) Humans can become so fixated on the future or the past that we forget about the *now.* We have a tendency to become fixated on ideas of how life should be. In states of hopelessness, these ideas not only take up permanent residence in our mind but also become our constant companion. These thoughts run nonstop in our head.

One of the best ways to overcome this is to practice being fully present in the moment and start *feeling* and *sensing* again. So, when you are driving, you focus on driving: how your foot feels on the gas pedal, how your hands feel on the wheel, and how your body feels sitting in the driver's seat. Simultaneously, you are completely focused on what other drivers are doing around you from a strictly observational standpoint. This practice of bringing your full and complete attention to what you are actually doing rather than to your thoughts is a form of meditation. It begins to dissolve your addiction to mental processing as your sole way of interacting with and getting along in the world, and it opens you to the possibility of a fuller and more complete experience of life.

There are formal practices, such as sitting meditation, tai chi, and qigong, that have been in place for centuries to aid humans in overcoming the pain associated with a strictly mind-based existence. More recently, MBSR (Mindfulness-Based Stress Reduction) has become popular, offered through universities and hospitals to help people combat stress, anxiety, and issues such as chronic pain and fatigue. There is a rapidly growing field of study proving the effectiveness of mindfulness and meditation.[3] Through a consistent, committed practice, participants report markedly increased peace, ease, and joy in life.

With this also comes equanimity toward emotion. We come to accept happiness or sadness, or contentment or loneliness, in any particular moment. These emotions are all a part of life. Further, one feeling is not better than another, even though we will judge it so. In fact, many people mistakenly believe that those who thrive only feel happiness, excitement, and contentment. This couldn't be further from the truth. The people who thrive experience *all* the emotions, but rather than judging them as good or bad, or being weighed down by them, they simply see them as "pointers"—gravity that is asking for their attention.

Hope Grows

In 2010, when the earthquake happened in Haiti, thousands of people were left without food, shelter, or hope of a brighter day. I called my close friend General Robert Worley, who was at the Pentagon, and asked for a C-130 aircraft to be filled with supplies to assist in this relief effort. He was able to connect me to a relief organization to deliver needed supplies to help the people of Haiti. Within two weeks, we had thousands of protein drinks aboard a plane.

I then called another friend, Dr. Elia Gourgouris, and said, "Let's go do some good!" He was ready to go, and so we went with packed supply bags.

We flew to the Dominican Republic and then cabbed seven hours to the border of Haiti to cross and connect with those in need. We finally arrived to stay in a house that now sheltered a new "family" of four adults and seventy-five children and babies. We slept on the floor of the balcony.

For both Elia and me, it was a mock crisis to watch the people's tremendous relief upon receiving the goods we shipped, while gaining some insight into their view of the world as people of a developing nation. Elia and I received a great blessing in this—but we also realized that life is short and precious. It renewed our appreciation for our friends and families back home and for the incredible fortunes we enjoy every day as Americans. Upon departure, we couldn't wait to get back to the States and to love on our families with gratefulness and a renewed passion.

Sometimes the givers are the biggest receivers of what life has to offer. I will never forget the looks of those kids who showed joy, laughter, and gratitude in such terrible circumstances. Their simple gratitude was enough to give many others hope and to remind us to cultivate gratitude amid our own life storms.

Children are a great inspiration for hope. They look at everything with excitement and anticipation because there are so many wondrous things in the world and they have an entire future ahead of them! They dream big about what and who they're going to be. They look forward to each day because it's full of discovery.

As we grow up and become adults, we tend to lose this sense of wonder. We also tend to think we should arrive at a particular "destination." Yet adulthood is not a place where we arrive. Furthermore, abandoning "childish" hopes and dreams is actually counterproductive. In fact, as we do grow up and grow older, we must continue chasing our hopes and dreams as we did when we were young.

We grow up and forget that we are wired to create. We respond to outdated programming that tells us to neglect our dreams and desires because we're adults now. It's essential to have hopes and aspirations, whether you're nine or ninety—even if you've achieved many great things in your lifetime. Otherwise, you can begin to flounder and become complacent.

Just as children need things in front of them to keep them occupied, adults, too, need purpose and learning in their lives. We need to be solidly anchored to a sense of purpose and hope. Otherwise, we risk falling away from the true course our life should take. In a sense, when we give up on hope, we take ourselves out of the game of life.

People without hope make themselves miserable and ill—and they do the same to those around them. When people start nosing into other people's business, it's because they don't have their own canvas—their own hope and life. I see this behavior frequently in older people. When someone is obsessed with the difficulties of aging or the events of other people's lives, I tell them they just need to get a life! Too much gossip or involvement in everyone else's business is a sign that we're not investing enough in our own life. We all need to have our own stuff going on, throughout our life, in order to maintain vitality and youthfulness.

The great news is that other people can come along and give us hope. They can lend us their canvas to paint on for a little while until we find our own. We can give people hope, and we can receive hope from them. If we are to thrive in life, we must refuse to give up on hope—no matter what pressure we are under. Life throws us obstacles and challenges, and it's up to us to hang on to hope since it's the foundation for getting us through those times.

I learned that I couldn't let life squash my hope when doctors told Marsha and me that our son Brandon wouldn't live through childhood, then adolescence. Three decades later, he's still here. I just never gave up. I never allowed anyone to take away our hope. Brandon's terminal diagnosis made it challenging to believe that we could care for and help him, especially because everyone in the medical field told us it was hopeless. There was no definitive explanation for his condition, and there were no answers. And even though we couldn't find answers, I had to choose a belief that ran against what so many people believe. I had to choose not to give up on hope and to live my life to the fullest each day. It also helped that Brandon had such a tenacity to live, so we borrowed his canvas on days where we couldn't paint on ours.

Sometimes people give up and say they have no other choice. They throw their hands up and give in. But there's *always* another choice. To say a tragedy or a disease will rule or ruin your life is just one perspective that is usually spoken from a place of fear or deep despair. The way I see it is that you are standing in the midst of much potential discovery and greatness. Hope is what will allow you to find it.

Planting the Seeds of Hope

Hope, like many great qualities, is sown in childhood. As I mentioned earlier, I have a strong faith in God and the Bible. My wife and I have often turned to the Bible and prayer for direction in our life and parenting. One of my favorite verses, which has guided us throughout our parenting, is Proverbs 22:6. It says: "Train up a child in the way he should go; and when he is old, he will not depart from it" (NKJV).

The phrase *train up* literally means to restrict but not choke. Picture a stake you would use to bolster a tomato plant to allow it to grow and bear fruit. When a tomato plant starts growing, it is only a stalk and leaves. When the fruit begins to grow, it becomes too heavy for the stalk. Without support, the fruit will fall to the ground and rot. The purpose of the stake is to prop up the fruit and prevent it from falling, so the entire plant can thrive and mature.

The stake is a metaphor for the gentle structure children require in order to grow up with hope, among other characteristics. The goal in raising a child is to provide the support they need to thrive. Parenting can either destroy hope or feed it.

Ideally, what we're trying to do in parenting is to train a child upward to be the best human he or she can be. This implies that when we are born, we're already falling downward. It is true that selfishness is already in our DNA, but so is cooperation. Training kids to do what's right, then, is teaching them that there is more to consider in life than just their needs; that is part of the discipline process. When discipline is handled correctly, children grow up with the sense that they belong to something larger—a family or a community—and they understand that their actions affect others. If discipline is administered too harshly or without explanation, it destroys their hope. Likewise, if you let your children run wild without guidance and the supportive structure of discipline, they will fail to thrive.

Maybe you are not a parent. You can still make a difference in the lives of the people around you. In fact, it's never too late to start mentoring someone. But what if you didn't receive the solid parenting that I just described? In that case, you might look for someone to mentor you. A mentor is basically a person who walks through life with you and is available to support you with guidance and wisdom. They have more life experience than you and a willingness to help you through the storms. They provide hope. Mentoring takes a lot of patience and time, but the payoff is priceless. The parenting process is where hope is made or broken, but fortunately, other people, such as mentors, can come to our aid where parenting has failed.

Grow Your Own Hope

One of the best ways to become encouraged—and nurture hope—is to encourage others. Get out of yourself! If you don't think your life has meaning or hope, serve somebody and you'll feel more hopeful instantly. Visit the elderly, volunteer, read books to kids—just do something, and you'll find that those positive feelings come back to you.

We're all born with a measure of faith in ourselves, in humanity, and in life. The issue is, will we live out that faith? Or will our faith be squelched by fear, anger, and anxiety? If your parents didn't build hope in you, you can build it in yourself.

As long as you are able to rest properly, you can never burn out on giving because you will be rewarded in more ways than you can imagine! Of course, this isn't the goal, but you will harvest what you plant, time after time. If you plant an apple seed, you'll get an apple tree. But if you're constantly tearing people down, belittling them and criticizing them, you're pulling out what could be a fruitful plant and leaving space for a weed to grow. You can't hope for a good harvest from a neglected garden full of weeds. There are so many critical lessons you will learn from the nurturing process, and it's easier to do it right starting as early as possible in life. But it's never too late to begin sowing good seeds now.

When my son Brent was five or six years old, the movie *Batman* was coming out and all he wanted for Christmas was a toy Batmobile. They were hard to find because the movie was not even in theaters yet, but I found one and brought it home. When I showed it to Brent, he was so excited! I asked him, "How many little boys do you think will never get a toy like this for Christmas . . . or ever?" I told him that I was giving the toy to him, just as I gave him his other toys, his house, and even his brother. The gift was unmerited; Brent hadn't earned the toy in any way. And the gift was extravagant in some ways; he obviously couldn't purchase it on his own. Like any child his age, Brent couldn't conceive of this at the time. But I was really trying to teach him the lesson that it's not just about you; it's about "us."

Several days later, I told Brent that we were going to drive to inner-city Detroit and give the Batmobile away to another boy. Brent, of course, begged me not to do it, but we did. We went to Detroit, driving through the city until we found a little boy and his mom on the street. We stopped and gave the Batmobile to this boy, who, along with his mom, was so amazed that he didn't think we were for real.

Brent thought the Batmobile was gone forever. But, lo and behold, on Christmas morning, he opened his presents and found another one. He thought it was the greatest thing that had ever happened to him! And he learned that what you give away, you always get back—whether it's something intangible, such as good feelings of charity or gratefulness for what you have, or tangible, such as a new toy.

Just a few years later, Brent was going on mission trips, giving of himself to others in need. He had already become a great person who cares deeply about people. He was *raised up* to believe in hope and that what he gives to people really does matter.

Faith, Hope, and Love

I've watched hope leave people when a crisis or tragedy hits. They just stop functioning, because life as they know it is over. In fact, what they know and have become accustomed to *is* over. But life itself doesn't have to be over. Refusing to give up hope allows new life to spring forth. Like planting a seed in the ground, a tragedy asks us to let go of the life we once had while waiting for new life to come.

In addition to degrees in psychology, I also have a background in theology. I studied theology because I wanted to fully understand life, and I believe psychology provides only part of the picture. The New Testament book of 1 Corinthians presents the greatest definition of love I've ever seen. In chapter 13, Saint Paul says you may have immense power or knowledge or wealth, but without love, your life is nothing. The passage concludes by saying, "And now abide faith, hope, love, these three; but the greatest of these is love" (1 Corinthians 13:13, NKJV). You may solve many mysteries or move mountains, but love is the purpose of life.

Another Bible passage, Hebrews 11:1, says: "Now faith is the substance of things hoped for, the evidence of things not seen" (NKJV). Faith is the substance—the paint on the brush—of the things we hope for. But hope is the canvas that faith is painted on. And what we ultimately hope for is love: the unconditional acceptance *from* others and *for* others. In the Greek language, three types of love exist: *philia*, the love of friendship and family; *eros*, the love of sex and passion; and *agape*, a godlike unconditional love or acceptance, and the deepest kind of love. All three types of love instill meaning and purpose in our lives.

So love is the ultimate goal, and it takes faith to live, but hope is the central part of this "trinity" that is manifested through time. It's mentioned in the middle of the Bible passage from 1 Corinthians that I shared, not as a bookend. Hope is in between two very important words—it's the glue that holds together faith and love. And our hope comes to life in the words we use, the choices we make, and the heart we bring to our relationships.

If we are to move beyond stress and toward a brighter future, we must have hope. As such, we need to make sure we have hope in something greater than ourselves. If we only hope in ourselves, we are limited. Hoping—and working—for success or beauty will feel empty at the end of life. So what if we made all of this money or accumulated nice things or turned heads every time we walked into a room? The measure of our life will be more about the people we have affected positively, and hope allows us to continue giving selflessly to this end.

PERFORMANCE-BOOSTING STRATEGIES

1. Are there any areas of life where you have lost hope? If so, take a moment to run through the 4-Step Process of Inspired Change (described in chapter 9). Conduct a mock crisis and identify which of your needs aren't being met because of MESP misalignment. Determine the needs you want to meet and write out an MESP alignment for those.
2. What is your life purpose? Identify how regaining hope in this area will help you with your life goals and support your life purpose.

CONCLUSION

The Beauty of Balance

The journey home from any disaster relief effort can be profoundly stressful and even confusing. You look forward to home, family, and normalcy. But your heart, mind, and body are still processing the horrors you've just witnessed—the lives lost, relationships severed, and homes, property, and natural areas destroyed. Even as the airplane lifted into the clouds over Bangkok and I knew that within hours, my family and friends would be greeting me with a warm welcome, my emotions raced from guilt to sorrow to relief and back to guilt again.

The last leg of the flight from Los Angeles to South Florida was particularly painful as I tried to grasp all that had happened and write down my thoughts, feelings, and impressions. Images flooded my mind: the wall covered with thousands of photos of missing babies and adults . . . the many destroyed villages . . . the mud-caked survivors in tattered clothes . . . children without parents . . . huge boats swept two miles inland . . . the sea floating with odd things like suitcases and Starbucks coffee machines . . . full-grown palm trees, washed out to sea. And would I ever forget the smells, such as the decaying corpses at the temple morgue mixed with Thai cooking at the "coffin café"?

This volatile mix of images, smells, and emotions exploded in me as I gazed at the peaceful sky outside the aircraft window. Although I knew I could never erase them from my heart, I also knew that my tsunami relief experiences would give me a greater ability to inspire other disaster survivors with hope and the assurance of better days ahead.

My long flights to and from Thailand were shared with Hollywood action star Jean-Claude van Damme, who came to Bangkok to help raise support for tsunami victims. Jean-Claude was a bright spot in my three-week Thailand trip. I enjoyed talking with the actor and his family, even signing a book for him and his son on the flight. And I remembered many fun moments watching him in his wild and wonderful action films.

Of course, it's easier to watch destruction in a movie than to actually witness its effects, as I did in Phuket. But the philosophy of good stress teaches that every stressful situation can be positive and beneficial in the long run. Every stressful situation has moments of learning and growth—teachable moments. I had many of these in Thailand, and I expect to have many more along life's journey.

There isn't a day that passes that I don't think about Wat Yan Yao, with its extremely hot and steamy conditions and its death and devastation a pungent reality all around me. Every day I count my blessings, knowing that each day is a gift to be enjoyed to the fullest.

Performance under pressure is ultimately about enjoying the moments of each day. It's about understanding the awesome privilege we have to learn from our experiences and to share them with other people. If you want to master life, you will need to become a master student of life. Thriving requires openness, along with a willingness to learn and to attend to all that comes your way with care. People who learn how to perform under pressure do not rush through things in life; they take their time and respond thoughtfully.

They also focus their mind and their heart on the positive aspects of reality, and they are grateful for the opportunity to participate fully in life.

Growing older is a true gift when you think of all the people who die young. Living each day with your end in view can crystallize your daily goals and keep them in focus. Start each day with purpose and reflect on your unique reason for being on the planet. Stay connected to this vitally important process. Meeting each day with joy and receptivity can provide a powerful release of passion and inspiration.

Many people lose their motivation to explore and pursue grand goals because they are disconnected from their life purpose and destiny. If we can stay in alignment, we will relax enough to simply let life develop around us—and thus be able to pursue our dreams and aspirations. Inspiration is within all of us from birth, and it manifests through spiritual connectedness to God (or what some may call a higher power), self, and others. Acting upon this can transform our lives.

When thoughts and beliefs align, powerful things happen. First, we develop an overwhelming sense of peace and fulfillment. Second, we hold the conviction that our thoughts and beliefs shape our actions—and that these actions lead to new realities that we, indeed, have a hand in creating. Third, we find a deep sense of belonging *to* life, from which service naturally flows. When we are in service to something greater than our own personal needs, our entire relationship with life shifts. We are then confident to face whatever comes, because we know it is inherently our destiny.

When I finally arrived back at my office and sat in the same seat that I had occupied only a few weeks before, I realized how much I had changed. It was the same office where I had spoken with my colleague Chris Galli upon first hearing of the tsunami only three weeks before, but now it looked and felt so different. During my time in Thailand, Chris had called regularly, knowing that I had been feeling alone and cut off from the rest of the world. Now I called him and related my mixed feelings to him—quite a bit different from the driven excitement I'd experienced a few weeks earlier, before my departure to Thailand.

I realized that I had come full circle from that day, and the difference was that my circle had grown enormously. Those few weeks in Thailand had given me what felt like years of learning. It was truly a life-changing experience that taught me to be aware of the gift of today—and to never take anything for granted, including my daily choice to respond positively to stress.

Life is precious and fleeting. Enjoying each day to the fullest by aligning with our life purpose can make living well a golden reality. Living gracefully also means living with no regrets and without looking back in remorse. The past is gone, and the future beckons seductively, waiting for us to write our destiny across its pristine pages.

In an overriding sense, this book is about balance, which is a beautiful principle. Think of a ballet dancer poised on the tip of his or her toe, body thrust forward, and arms spread like an eagle's wings. Balance is the key to performing under pressure and cracking our personal stress code. By balancing stress with recovery—and achieving balance by regularly aligning our mental, emotional, spiritual, and physical aspects—we can experience stress as a positive force that propels us to new heights.

Our commitment to regular practice enables us to forever change our relationship to stress and, therefore, live in the place where we are always falling forward—into delight, into joy, and into experience, even when there is sadness, grief, and overwhelm. Performing under pressure is about living life to its utmost. Balance is not a destination but a journey. It is a way of living consciously for optimum health and elite performance. And although the road may be bumpy and sometimes dark, there's always a spectacular sunrise on the horizon.

APPENDIX

Macronutrients and Your Health

Having proper nutrition is key to being able to master our stress and perform under pressure. If we are not feeding our body the healthy food it needs—at regular intervals—we will experience serious physical leakage.

My wife, Marsha Pitt Lyles, is a certified nutrition coach, professional dancer, cheerleader, trainer, author, and contributor to the *New York Times*. She has coached me on diet, exercise, and nutrition for many years—and in turn, I have coached thousands of people using her principles and tips for creating a healthy body.

Since diet is so important to overall performance and health, I've included more detailed information that I have learned from my wife about nutrition, particularly macronutrients. Macronutrients are so named because we need these nutrients in large amounts in order to function properly. Let's take a look at each one individually.

Carbohydrates

The Dietary Guidelines for Americans state that carbohydrates should comprise the largest part of our diet—up to 65 percent.[1] But you have to eat the right kind of carbohydrates: complex carbohydrates. Stay away from simple carbohydrates like refined white sugar, cookies, cakes, and white breads. Simple carbs elevate blood sugar, which increases blood glucose levels and causes the body to produce excess amounts of insulin. This will cause you to store fat. While simple carbs provide short-term bursts of energy, they will rapidly drop your energy levels, which may result in a slump that can negatively affect your mood.[2]

Instead of processed simple carbs like the ones I just described, eat complex carbohydrates like whole grains, beans, legumes, and vegetables. These forms of carbohydrates are high in fiber, which will keep you fuller for longer periods of time. While fruits are considered a simple carbohydrate, they are also full of fiber and contain vitamins that are excellent for your health. Stay away from fruit juices and dried fruit, which are concentrated forms of sugar and often contain added sugar. Furthermore, since all the water has been taken out of the dried varieties of fruit, one cup of raisins will contain much more sugar than one cup of grapes due to the water content.

Milk is also a simple carbohydrate. If you love milk, limit your intake to two cups of skim milk per day. There are many tasty milk substitutes like almond milk if you have a tolerance issue. If you don't like milk in any form, you can get plenty of calcium from sardines, sesame seeds, soybeans, dark-green leafy vegetables such as broccoli rabe, and fruits like kiwis, oranges, and tangerines.

Proteins

Protein is another important macronutrient. Where carbohydrates are the body's main source of energy, proteins are its building blocks. Protein is important for almost every cell function, and it is needed to build strong and lean muscle mass. Muscle mass is important to our body, because for every pound of lean muscle mass, the body burns three times as many calories as a pound of fat.[3] If you're lacking in protein intake, your body will respond with reduced muscle mass, which gives the body a flabby, saggy appearance. It also results in a lower metabolism, which leads to weight gain.

A lack of protein will give you a "foggy" brain as well, since protein intake helps slow down the time release of carbohydrates, which are the body's main source of energy. Protein allows the brain to get a steady stream of energy. If the body doesn't have enough protein to help the time release of carbohydrates, blood sugar will slide up too quickly and then crash, leaving you feeling weak and craving sweets. The repeated rise and fall of blood sugar can cause both weight gain and disease.[4]

Sources of protein are meat, fish, poultry, cheese, eggs, yogurt, and milk as well as grains, vegetables, nuts, and beans. The majority of nutritionists consider animal products to be the best sources of protein because they contain all nine essential amino acids. (There are twenty amino acids that the body must have to function. Nine cannot be synthesized by the body on its own. Therefore, these nine are called essential amino acids, as they must be obtained from our diet.)

Since plant proteins like vegetables, grains, nuts, beans, seeds, peas, and corn do not contain the nine essential amino acids like animal products do, vegetarians must get a wide range of plant proteins in order to meet their protein requirement. This is not difficult, however, for healthy vegetarians.

In fact, in February 2015, the Dietary Guidelines Advisory Committee released a report stating that a predominantly vegetarian diet (it included fish) was the only healthy and sustainable diet based on all evaluated factors, including health, nutrition, and environmental impact.[5] They noted that a significant reduction or elimination of meat and dairy products is imperative to address America's growing problem with the development of lifestyle diseases and the enormous pollution associated with animal agriculture. The Academy of Nutrition and Dietetics now says that a sound vegetarian diet with a wide variety of foods provides all the nutrients needed by the body.[6] Unlike with animal foods, our bodies are able to fully digest plant foods, while receiving all the important nutrients.

The bottom line: it is wise on many levels, health and performance included, that our diet be predominantly plant-based.

Fats

The last macronutrient that the body needs for survival is fat. Like carbohydrates, fats are another food group that often gets eliminated from the diet only to cause you to binge eat. Fats are what keep you satiated. They are also what give you that "finger-licking-good feeling" and create—along with a number of other factors—what is called "mouthfeel," or how good that food tastes and feels when it's in your mouth.

When manufacturers substitute fats with chemicals, including preservatives, to achieve reduced-fat products, they end up creating a "food" that leaves you feeling hungry and unsatisfied. (Remember, the more processed a "food" is, the less it is an actual food. So, in general, it is best to eat a whole food diet.)

Fats also provide energy, protect our organs, maintain cell membranes, and help the body absorb and process nutrients. A lack of fat in the diet can leave you with dry hair and skin. And studies have shown that a lack of omega-3 fatty acids like those found in salmon, mackerel, and sardines is associated with depression and impulsive behavior, which can lead to suicide, violence, and accidents.[7]

However, you have to eat good fat. What is the difference between good and bad fat? There are four major categories of fats: monounsaturated fat, polyunsaturated fat, saturated fat, and trans fat. The first two fats, monounsaturated and polyunsaturated fats, are the good fats. Good fats (like those in avocados, fish, nuts, and eggs) are important as they actually help our body to burn fat.

Examples of monounsaturated fats include olive, peanut, canola, sesame, and sunflower oils; macadamia nuts, cashews, pecans, pistachios, Brazil nuts, almonds, almond butter, peanuts, peanut butter, and cashew butter; seeds like pumpkin, flaxseed, sesame, and sunflower; fish like herring, salmon, and halibut; and cheeses like Parmesan, cream cheese, Roquefort, Muenster, and Monterey Jack. Other terrific sources are avocados and black and green olives.

For polyunsaturated fats, there are two types: omega-3 and omega-6. Omega-3 examples include ALA (found in flaxseed oil, hemp oil, and walnuts), EPA (found in marine sources), and DHA (found in marine oils like fish and egg oils), black beans, Brussels sprouts, canola oil, cauliflower, flaxseeds, herring, kidney beans, pasture-raised meats, salmon, sardines, shrimp, soybean oil, soybeans, tofu, trout, wild rice, and winter squash.

Examples of omega-6 polyunsaturated fats are acai berries, avocados, black-currant seed oil, borage oil, canola oil, cashews, cereals, coconut, corn oil, cottonseed oil, durum wheat, eggs, evening primrose oil, flax, hemp oil, linseed oil, nuts, pecans, pine nuts, poultry, pumpkin seeds, rapeseed, safflower oil, soybean oil, spirulina, sunflower seed oil, walnuts, and whole-grain breads.

The last two fats are saturated and trans fats. Examples of saturated fats are high-fat cuts of meat (beef, lamb, pork), chicken with skin, whole-fat dairy products (milk and cream), butter, cheese, ice cream, palm and coconut oils, and lard. Examples of trans fats are cookies, pastries, doughnuts, packaged snack foods (microwave popcorn, crackers, chips), vegetable shortening, fried foods (French fries, fried chicken, chicken nuggets, breaded fish), and candy bars.

The majority of your fats should be unsaturated, although some studies now report that the consumption of saturated fats doesn't increase the incidence of cardiovascular disease compared to people who eat less.[8] Whether or not you believe that saturated fats are all bad, the evidence is clear that if you eat a diet high in saturated fat and high in refined carbohydrates, you will be at risk for obesity and lifestyle-related diseases such as diabetes.

Be careful of "fake fats." If you eat real, organic butter, where the ingredients say organic cream and salt, you will enjoy that one piece of whole-wheat toast much more. You will feel satisfied and end up using less full-fat butter than you would the "reduced-fat" butter.

Avoid all fried foods, margarine and vegetable shortening, baked goods, and processed snack foods. Of course, you can have them every once in a while, but when you eat a well-balanced diet without leaving out any of the food groups, you will be less inclined to crave these foods.

While it is ideal to avoid fast-food restaurants and their foods at all costs, it may not be easy, especially if you do a lot of traveling for your work. Many grocery stores today have deli counters with premade foods and take-out fare with healthier choices than fast-food restaurants. Some stores even have salad bars. So consider these first.

Above all, eat mindfully and healthfully—choosing a wide variety of whole foods to give your body what it needs. Doing so will make all the difference in converting bad stress into good stress and learning to thrive under pressure.

Acknowledgments

This book was inspired and influenced by the many brave individuals and groups I have had the privilege of working with, side by side, across America and around the world, caring for those touched by tragedy and life's challenges. When I consider all who have touched me, I am truly humbled. I think about their names and faces often; they have inspired and influenced me profoundly, making my efforts with those whom I touch matter even more. Not a day goes by that I don't think about those affected by 9/11, as well as the Asian tsunami, Hurricane Katrina, and the Haiti earthquake. I'm also impacted by the brave men and women of our armed forces who struggle with PTSD (post-traumatic stress disorder) and related issues that were brought home from the theater of war. There are no words to describe my reverence for them and their journey of healing. I deeply respect and admire all the members of our armed forces and the numerous rescue and recovery teams that so proudly serve our country with courage and honor, in life and in sacrifice.

I extend deep, heartfelt thanks to all those individuals and organizations that support my efforts to help others when tragedy strikes; they make it possible for me to train others in how to cope with, and eventually overcome, the difficult life challenges that can touch any of us at any time, with or without warning. To those I have encountered in the destruction zones around the world, know that I will never forget you. Your faces and stories are ever fresh in my mind and alive, eternally, in my heart. As I travel across the United States, speaking and training individuals on the art of thriving, I speak of your inspiring courage and bravery. My extraordinary experiences with you have made me more whole.

A special thanks to my wife, Marsha; my sons, Brayden, Brandon, and Brent; and Mr. and Mrs. Pitt, my acquired mom and dad, in the absence of my deceased parents, for their support and belief in me and their vision of this book reaching the world to inspire positive change and hope. And thank you to the team at Southwestern Publishing Group.

My heartfelt appreciation also goes to Migdalia, who has mastered the art of chasing my weekly schedule. You are amazing. I extend a special appreciation and love to my siblings, Mary, Roger, Becky, and Dale, for all the childhood memories in the 'hood back in Indy.

Finally, I wish to acknowledge anyone who has dedicated themselves to the path of being the best they can be. Without you, my work would not exist, and I feel the utmost gratitude for the privilege of supporting you in living the life of your dreams.

Thank you all.

Endnotes

INTRODUCTION: A NEW LOOK AT AN OLD ISSUE

1. Agnese Mariotti, "The Effects of Chronic Stress on Health: New Insights into the Molecular Mechanisms of Brain-Body Communication," *Future Science OA* 1, no. 3 (November 2015): FSO23, https://doi.org/10.4155/fso.15.21.

2. Giuseppe Passarino, Francesco De Rango, and Alberto Montesanto, "Human Longevity: Genetics or Lifestyle? It Takes Two to Tango," *Immunity & Ageing* 13 (2016): 12, https://doi.org/10.1186/s12979-016-0066-z.

CHAPTER 1: SAY YES TO STRESS

1. Hilary Brueck, "From Birth to Old Age, Here's What Americans Are Most Likely to Die from at Every Age," *Business Insider,* June 17, 2018, https://www.businessinsider.com/how-youre-most-likely-to-die-at-every-age-2018-6.

2. "The World: Life Expectancy (2015) - Top 100+," Geoba.se, accessed August 1, 2015, http://www.geoba.se/population.php?pc=world&type=15.

3. S. Jay Olshansky, et al., "A Potential Decline in Life Expectancy in the United States in the 21st Century," *New England Journal of Medicine* 352 (2005): 1138-1145. doi: 10.1056/NEJMsr043743.

4. Christopher Bergland, "Cortisol: Why the 'Stress Hormone' Is Public Enemy Number 1," *Psychology Today,* January 22, 2013, https://www.psychologytoday.com/us/blog/the-athletes-way/201301/cortisol-why-the-stress-hormone-is-public-enemy-no-1.

5. Harvard Health Publishing, "Understanding the Stress Response," updated May 1, 2018, https://www.health.harvard.edu/staying-healthy/understanding-the-stress-response.

6. University College London, "Long-Term Stress Linked to Higher Levels of Obesity, Hair Samples Show: People Who Suffer Long-Term Stress May Also Be More Prone to Obesity," ScienceDaily, February 23, 2017, www.sciencedaily.com/releases/2017/02/170223092342.htm.

7. J. B. Lohr, et al., "Is Post-Traumatic Stress Disorder Associated with Premature Senescence? A Review of the Literature," *American Journal of Geriatric Psychiatry*, 23 (2015): 709–725, http://dx.doi.org/10.1016/j.jagp.2015.04.001.

   L. Ala-Mursula, et al., "Long-Term Unemployment Is Associated with Short Telomeres in 31-Year-Old Men: An Observational Study in the Northern Finland Birth Cohort 1966." *PLoS One* 8 (2013): e80094, https://doi.org/10.1371/journal.pone.0080094.

CHAPTER 2: THE GIFT OF GRAVITY

1. "The Power of Gravity," NASA, accessed January 15, 2019, https://www.hq.nasa.gov/pao/History/SP-4026/noord1.html.

2. Rhett Herman, "How Fast Is the Earth Moving?" *Scientific American,* accessed January 15, 2019, https://www.scientificamerican.com/article/how-fast-is-the-earth-mov/.

3. Chidi Akusobi, "Does Zero Gravity Exist in Space?" *Yale Scientific*, October 2, 2010, http://www.yalescientific.org/2010/10/mythbusters-does-zero-gravity-exist-in-space/.

4. Ibid.

5. "The Human Body in Space," NASA, accessed February 22, 2019, https://www.nasa.gov/hrp/bodyinspace.

CHAPTER 3: WHAT LIMITS YOUR PERFORMANCE?

1. Benjamin Gardner et al., "Making Health Habitual: The Psychology of 'Habit-Formation' and General Practice," *British Journal of General Practice* 62, no. 605 (December 2012): 664-66, https://doi.org/10.3399/bjgp12X659466.

CHAPTER 4: A ROADMAP FOR STRESS RECOVERY

1. Drake Baer, "Why You Need to Unplug Every 90 Minutes," *Fast Company,* June 19, 2013, https://www.fastcompany.com/3013188/why-you-need-to-unplug-every-90-minutes.

2. Ibid.

3. "How Much Sleep Do We Really Need?" National Sleep Foundation, accessed on February 16, 2019, https://www.sleepfoundation.org/excessivesleepiness/content/how-much-sleep-do-we-really-need-0.

4. Baer, "Why You Need to Unplug."

5. Jeffrey M. Jones, "In U.S., 40% Get Less Than Recommended Amount of Sleep," Gallup, December 29, 2013, https://news.gallup.com/poll/166553/less-recommended-amount-sleep.aspx.

6. "Caffeine Metabolism," Caffeineinformer, accessed February 5, 2019, https://www.caffeineinformer.com/caffeine-metabolism.

7. Sharon M. O'Brien, MPAS, PA-C, "Watching the Clock Can Worsen Insomnia," *Clinical Advisor,* January 20, 2012, https://www.clinicaladvisor.com/the-waiting-room/watching-the-clock-can-worsen-insomnia/article/224124/.

8. Kevin Loria, "Most Scientists Say You Shouldn't Hit the Snooze Button—Here's How to Snooze the Right Way," *Business Insider,* May 21, 2017, https://www.businessinsider.com/snooze-button-effect-on-sleep-2017-5.

CHAPTER 5: MANAGING EMOTIONS, MAXIMIZING ENERGY

1. Dictionary.com, s.v. "Emotion," accessed February 5, 2019, https://www.dictionary.com/browse/emotion.

2. Hara Estroff Marano, "Our Brain's Negative Bias," *Psychology Today,* published June 20, 2003, last reviewed June 9, 2016, https://www.psychologytoday.com/us/articles/200306/our-brains-negative-bias.

3. Roland N. Pittman, "Oxygen Transport in the Microcirculation and Its Regulation," *Microcirculation* 20, no. 2 (February 2013): 117-37, https://doi.org/10.1111/micc.12017.

CHAPTER 7: MANAGING THE BODY AND PHYSICAL STRESS

1. Robert Kress, RPh, "Stress, Inflammation, Immunity," rn.com, AMN Healthcare Education Services, accessed January 9, 2019, https://www.rn.com/featured-stories/stress-inflammation-immunity/.

2. Michael Anft, "Understanding Inflammation," *Johns Hopkins Health Review* 3, no. 1 (Spring/Summer 2016), https://www.johnshopkinshealthreview.com/issues/spring-summer-2016/articles/understanding-inflammation.

3. Teresa Carr, "Too Many Meds? America's Love Affair with Prescription Medication," *Consumer Reports,* August 3, 2017, https://www.consumerreports.org/prescription-drugs/too-many-meds-americas-love-affair-with-prescription-medication/.

4. Matt Richtel and Andrew Jacobs, "American Adults Just Keep Getting Fatter," *New York Times,* March 23, 2018, https://www.nytimes.com/2018/03/23/health/obesity-us-adults.html.

5. Debra L. Blackwell, PhD, "State Variation in Meeting the 2008 Federal Requirements for Both Aerobic and Muscle-Strengthening through Leisure-Time Physical Activity among Adults Aged 18–64: United States, 2010–2015," *National Health Statistics Reports,* no 112 (June 2018), https://www.cdc.gov/nchs/data/nhsr/nhsr112.pdf.

6. National Center for Health Statistics, "Selected Health Conditions and Risk Factors, by Age: United States, Selected Years 1988–1994 through 2015–2016," accessed January 22, 2019, https://www.cdc.gov/nchs/fastats/obesity-overweight.htm.

7. "Diabetes, Heart Disease, and You," Centers for Disease Control, November 23, 2016, https://www.cdc.gov/features/diabetes-heart-disease/index.html.

8. "Carbohydrates and Blood Sugar," the Nutrition Source, Harvard T. H. Chan School of Public Health, accessed March 13, 2019, https://www.hsph.harvard.edu/nutritionsource/carbohydrates/carbohydrates-and-blood-sugar/.

9. Katie Adolphus, Clare L. Lawton, and Louise Dye, "The Effects of Breakfast on Behavior and Academic Performance in Children and Adolescents," *Frontiers in Human Neuroscience* 7 (2013): 425, https://doi.org/10.3389/fnhum.2013.00425.

10. Hilary Brueck, "The Best Time of Day to Do Everything at Work, According to Science," *Business Insider,* August 13, 2018, https://www.businessinsider.com/best-time-day-work-according-to-science-2018-5.

11. Kris Gunnars, "6 Graphs That Show Why the 'War' on Fat Was a Huge Mistake," Healthline, November 4, 2013, https://www.healthline.com/nutrition/6-graphs-the-war-on-fat-was-a-mistake#section2.

12. "Low-Carb, High-Protein Diets," Harvard Health Publishing, July 2015, https://www.health.harvard.edu/healthy-eating/low-carb-high-protein-diets.

13. "The Right Plant-Based Diet for You," Harvard Health Publishing, January 2018, https://www.health.harvard.edu/staying-healthy/the-right-plant-based-diet-for-you.

14. Gabriella Boston, "The Many Benefits of Walking 30 Minutes a Day," *Washington Post,* October 20, 2015, https://www.washingtonpost.com/lifestyle/wellness/the-many-benefits-of-walking-30-minutes-a-day/2015/10/19/cf12c938-71e1-11e5-9cbb-790369643cf9_story.html?utm_term=.05e42cbe41a2.

15. "Depression and anxiety: Exercise eases symptoms," Mayo Clinic, October 10, 2014, http://www.mayoclinic.org/diseases-conditions/depression/in-depth/depression-and-exercise/art-20046495.

16. US Department of Health and Human Services, *Physical Activity Guidelines for Americans (2nd Edition),* (Washington, DC, 2018), https://health.gov/paguidelines/second-edition/pdf/Physical_Activity_Guidelines_2nd_edition.pdf, accessed January 23, 2019.

17. Ibid.

CHAPTER 8: TAMING TECHNOSTRESS

1. "Distracted Driving Triples Crash Risk," CBS New York, April 6, 2017, https://newyork.cbslocal.com/2017/04/05/study-distracted-driving-triples-crash-risk/.

2. David Perlmutter and Alberto Villoldo, *Power Up Your Brain: The Neuroscience of Enlightenment* (Carlsbad, CA: Hay House, 2012).

3. Tim Adams, "Interview: Norman Doidge: the Man Teaching Us to Change Our Minds," *Guardian,* February 8, 2015, https://www.theguardian.com/science/2015/feb/08/norman-doidge-brain-healing-neuroplasticity-interview.

4. Michael Vaughan, "Know Your Limits, Your Brain Can Only Take So Much," *Entrepreneur,* January 21, 2014, https://www.entrepreneur.com/article/230925.

5. "Stress and Anxiety in the Digital Age: the Dark Side of Technology," the Open University, updated May 23, 2018, https://www.open.edu/openlearn/health-sports-psychology/mental-health/managing-stress-and-anxiety-the-digital-age-the-dark-side-technology.

CHAPTER 11: HOPE IS THE CANVAS OF LIFE

1. Faith Brynie, PhD, "The Placebo Effect: How It Works," *Psychology Today,* January 10, 2012, https://www.psychologytoday.com/us/blog/brain-sense/201201/the-placebo-effect-how-it-works.

2. Cecilia C. Schiavon, et al., "Optimism and Hope in Chronic Disease: A Systematic Review," *Frontiers in Psychology* 7 (2016): 2022, https://doi.org/10.3389/fpsyg.2016.02022.

3. S. Banthand and M. D. Ardebil, "Effectiveness of Mindfulness Meditation on Pain and Quality of Life with Patients with Chronic Low Back Pain," *International Journal of Yoga* 8, no. 2 (July–December 2015): 128-33, https://doi.org/10.4103/0973-6131.158476.

APPENDIX: MACRONUTRIENTS AND YOUR HEALTH

1. Office of Disease Prevention and Health Promotion, "Daily Nutritional Goals for Age-Sex Groups Based on Dietary Reference Intakes and Dietary Guidelines Recommendations," table A7-1 in *Dietary Guidelines for Americans*, 2015–2020, 8th ed., accessed March 18, 2019, https://health.gov/dietaryguidelines/2015/guidelines/appendix-7/.

2. "Simple vs Complex Carbs," diabetes.co.uk, accessed January 8, 2019, https://www.diabetes.co.uk/nutrition/simple-carbs-vs-complex-carbs.html.

3. Paige Waehner, "How Many Calories Does Muscle Really Burn?" Verywell Fit, updated February 7, 2019, https://www.verywellfit.com/how-many-calories-does-muscle-really-burn-1231074.

4. "Here's What Happens to Your Body When You Don't Eat Enough Protein," *Shape,* March 2, 2017, https://www.shape.com.sg/health/heres-what-happens-your-body-when-you-dont-eat-enough-protein/.

5. US Department of Health and Human Services and US Department of Agriculture, *Scientific Report of the 2015 Dietary Guidelines Advisory Committee*, February 2015, http://www.health.gov/dietaryguidelines/2015-scientific-report/pdfs/scientific-report-of-the-2015-dietary-guidelines-advisory-committee.pdf.

6. "Vegetarian Diets Can Help Prevent Chronic Diseases, American Dietetic Association Says," *Science Daily*, July 3, 2009, http://www.sciencedaily.com/releases/2009/07/090701103002.htm.

7. Sarah M. Conklin et al., "Serum Omega-3 Fatty Acids Are Associated with Variation in Mood, Personality and Behavior in Hypercholesterolemic Community Volunteers," *Psychiatry Research* 152, no. 1 (2007): 1–10. https://doi.org/10.1016/j.psychres.2006.10.006.

8. Patty W. Siri-Tarino et al., "Meta-Analysis of Prospective Cohort Studies Evaluating the Association of Saturated Fat with Cardiovascular Disease," *American Journal of Clinical Nutrition* 91, no. 3 (2010): 535–546, https://doi.org/10.3945/ajcn.2009.27725.

   R. Chowdhury et al., "Association of Dietary, Circulating, and Supplement Fatty Acids with Coronary Risk: A Systematic Review and Meta-Analysis," *Annals of Medicine* 160, no. 6 (2014): 398–406, https://doi.org/10.7326/M13-1788.

Notes

NOTES